GEOMETRY FOR BEGINNERS

The Ultimate Step by Step Guide to Acing Geometry

By

Reza Nazari

Published by: **Effortless Math Education**

for Online Math Practice Visit www.EffortlessMath.com

Welcome to
Geometry Prep
2024

Thank you for choosing Effortless Math for your Geometry preparation and congratulations on making the decision to take the Geometry course! It's a remarkable move you are taking, one that shouldn't be diminished in any capacity.

That's why you need to use every tool possible to ensure you succeed on the test with the highest possible score, and this extensive study guide is one such tool.

Geometry for Beginners is meticulously structured to encompass all the topics typically found in an introductory Geometry course. This book presents clear and concise explanations along with illustrative examples to elucidate geometric concepts, making it an invaluable resource for learners starting their journey in Geometry.

This comprehensive study guide for Geometry offers flexibility for various learning environments—it can complement traditional classroom instruction or serve as a complete self-study guide. This book equips you with a solid foundation in Geometry, preparing you to excel in this subject and build confidence in your mathematical abilities. With the help of Geometry for Beginners, mastering the fundamentals of Geometry is within your reach.

How to Use This Book Effectively

Look no further when you need a study guide to improve your math skills to succeed on the Geometry test. Each chapter of this comprehensive guide to the Geometry will provide you with the knowledge, tools, and understanding needed for every topic covered on the course.

It's imperative that you understand each topic before moving onto another one, as that's the way to guarantee your success. Each chapter provides you with examples and a step-by-step guide of every concept to better understand the content that will be on the course. To get the best possible results from this book:

➢ **Begin studying long before your test date**. This provides you ample time to learn the different math concepts. The earlier you begin studying for the test, the sharper your skills will be. Do not procrastinate! Provide yourself with plenty of time to learn the concepts and feel comfortable that you understand them when your test date arrives.

➢ **Practice consistently**. Study Geometry concepts at least 20 to 30 minutes a day. Remember, slow and steady wins the race, which can be applied to preparing for the Geometry test. Instead of cramming to tackle everything at once, be patient and learn the math topics in short bursts.

➢ Whenever you get a math problem wrong, **mark it off, and review it later** to make sure you understand the concept.

➢ Start each session by **looking over the previous material.**

➢ Once you've reviewed the book's lessons, **take a practice test at the back of the book** to gauge your level of readiness. Then, review your results. Read detailed answers and solutions for each question you missed.

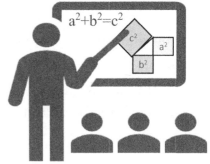

➢ **Take another practice test** to get an idea of how ready you are to take the actual exam. Taking the practice tests will give you the confidence you need on test day. Simulate the Geometry testing environment by sitting in a quiet room free from distraction. Make sure to clock yourself with a timer.

Looking for more?

Visit <u>EffortlessMath.com/Geometry</u> to find hundreds of Geometry worksheets, video tutorials, practice tests, Geometry formulas, and much more.

Or scan this QR code.

No Registration Required.

Contents

CHAPTER

1 Geometric Tools and Concepts

Math topics that you'll learn in this chapter:

- ☑ Points, Lines, and Planes
- ☑ Line Segments and Measurements
- ☑ Midpoint and distance
- ☑ Parallel Lines and Transversals
- ☑ Perpendicular Lines
- ☑ Lines, Rays, and Angles
- ☑ Types of Angles
- ☑ Complementary and Supplementary angles
- ☑ Bisecting an Angle
- ☑ Constructing a Triangle Given Its Sides
- ☑ The Circumscribed Circle
- ☑ The Inscribed Circle of a Triangle
- ☑ Inscribing Regular Polygons

Points, Lines, and Planes

- Points: A point in geometry represents a specific location. It does not have any dimension—no width, no length, and no depth. A point is typically represented by a dot and is often labeled with a capital letter.

•A

- Lines: A line in geometry is a straight one-dimensional figure that has no beginning or end, extending indefinitely in both directions. It's defined by any two points on the line. You can name a line by any two points on the line, such as $\overleftrightarrow{AB}$ or $\overleftrightarrow{BA}$, or by a single lowercase letter, (Line l).

- Planes: A plane in geometry is a flat, two-dimensional surface that extends infinitely in all directions. A plane is usually named by three non-collinear points lying on it— for example, plane ABC, or by a capital letter (Plane P).

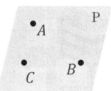

Examples:

What are two other ways to name $\overleftrightarrow{DE}$?

What are three other ways to name Plane G?

What are the names of three collinear points?

What are the names of four coplanar points?

Solution:

Two other ways to name $\overleftrightarrow{DE}$ are $\overleftrightarrow{ED}$ and line z.

Two other ways to name Plane G are Plane ABE, Plane CBA and Plane AEC.

Points B, E, and C are collinear.

Points A, B, C, and E are coplanar

Line Segments and Measurements

- A line segment in geometry is a part of a line that is bounded by two distinct end points and contains every point on the line between its endpoints. Unlike a line, it does not extend indefinitely but has a definitive start and end. For example, if you have points A and B, you could refer to the line segment as segment AB.

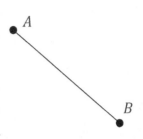

- To measure a line segment, you can use tools like a ruler, aligning one endpoint with the zero mark and reading the length at the other endpoint.

- Notice: Furthermore, if a point C exists between A and B on a line segment, the Segment Addition Postulate applies. It states that the total length of segment AB is the sum of segments AC and CB ($AB = AC + CB$). This rule can assist in calculating unknown segment lengths in various geometric problems.

Examples:

Example 1. Use a ruler to measure the line segments in centimeters, rounding results to the nearest centimeter.

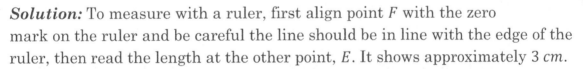

Solution: To measure with a ruler, first align point F with the zero mark on the ruler and be careful the line should be in line with the edge of the ruler, then read the length at the other point, E. It shows approximately $3\ cm$.

Example 2. In the figure below, line segment AB is 12 units long. Point C lies between points A and B such that line segment AC is twice as long as line segment CB. Find the lengths of line segments AC and CB.

Solution: To solve this problem, let's denote the length of line segment CB as x. According to the problem, line segment AC is twice as long, so its length is $2x$. Since line segment AB is the entire length, and it equals 12 units, we can set up the following equation: $2x + x = 12 \rightarrow 3x = 12 \rightarrow x = 4$

Solving this equation gives $x = 4$ units. So, the length of line segment CB is 4 units, and the length of line segment AC is 8 units.

Midpoint and Distance

- **Midpoint:** On a number line, the midpoint is the exact center point between two given points. Given two numbers a and b on the number line, the midpoint M is the average of a and b. Mathematically, this is represented as: $M = \frac{a+b}{2}$

  For example, if a is 2 and b is 8, the midpoint M would be $\frac{2+8}{2} = 5$.

  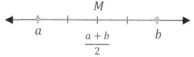

- **Distance:** The distance between two points on a number line is the absolute difference between those numbers. Given two numbers a and b, the distance d between them is: $d = |b - a|$

  Where the vertical bars represent the absolute value, ensuring the distance is always positive. For instance, the distance between 3 and 8 would be $|8 - 3| = 5$.

Examples:

Example 1. The length of the line segment is 18 cm, find the midpoint of this line segment.

$$\overset{18\,cm}{\underset{A \qquad\qquad\qquad B}{\rule{5cm}{0.4pt}}}$$

Solution: When working with a one-dimensional line segment (like a segment on a ruler or a number line), finding the midpoint is a matter of determining half its length.

The distance from one end of the segment to the midpoint would be half the total length of the segment.

Distance to midpoint $= \frac{Total\ Length}{2} = \frac{18\ cm}{2} = 9\ cm$

So, if you start at one end of the segment and measure 9 cm, you will reach the midpoint. The midpoint of this line segment is 9 cm from either end.

Example 2. Consider two points on the number line, $C = -3$ and $D = 5$. Find the distance between these two points.

Solution: To find the distance between two points on a number line, we simply take the absolute difference between their values.

$$d = |D - C| = |5 - (-3)| = |5 + 3| = |8| = 8$$

The distance between points C and D on the number line is 8 units.

Parallel lines and Transversals

- Parallel lines are two lines in a plane that never intersect or meet. They remain the same distance apart over their entire length.

- A transversal, in the context of geometry, is a line that intersects two or more other lines in the plane, at distinct points.

- When a line (transversal) intersects two parallel lines in the same plane, eight angles are formed. In the following diagram, a transversal intersects two parallel lines. Angles $1, 3, 5,$ and 7 are congruent. Angles $2, 4, 6,$ and 8 are also congruent.

- In the following diagram, the following angles are supplementary angles (their sum is 180):

  - Angles 1 and 8
  - Angles 2 and 7
  - Angles 3 and 6
  - Angles 4 and 5

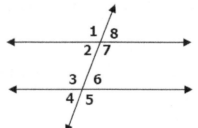

Example:

In the following diagram, two parallel lines are cut by a transversal. What is the value of x?

Solution: The two angles $3x - 15$ and $2x + 7$ are equivalent.

That is: $3x - 15 = 2x + 7$

Now, solve for x:

$3x - 15 + 15 = 2x + 7 + 15$

$\rightarrow 3x = 2x + 22 \rightarrow 3x - 2x = 2x + 22 - 2x \rightarrow$
$x = 22$

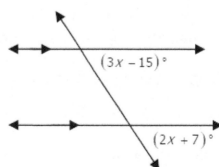

Perpendicular Lines

- In geometry, a line is said to be perpendicular to another line if the two lines intersect at a right angle. Constructing perpendicular lines requires specific tools like a straightedge and a compass. For construct a line perpendicular to QR passing through point S. follow these steps:

  - **Choose the Point:** Let's use point S on line segment QR as our base.

  - **Drawing arcs with Compass:** With S as the center and a suitable radius, draw an arc to the left and right of line QR, creating points A and B respectively.

  - **Drawing Additional Arcs:** Without adjusting the compass width, place the compass point on A and draw a semi-arc above the line QR. Similarly, place the compass point on B and draw a semi-arc below the line QR. These arcs should intersect, creating a point we'll label as T.

    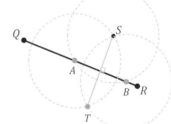

  - **Drawing the Perpendicular Line:** Using your straightedge, draw a line from S through point T. This line, labeled ST, is perpendicular to QR at point S.

- Notice: The line segment ST is perpendicular to line segment QR at point S. The angle between ST and QR is 90 degrees.

Example:

Draw a perpendicular line from point E on the line AB.

Solution: Place the compass point on E and draw a semicircle that intersects line AB in two points. Let's call these two points C and D.
Increase the width of the compass a little, place the compass point on C and draw a small arc above and below line AB.

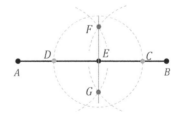

Without changing the compass width again, place the compass point on D and draw a small arc so that it intersects the previous arc drawn from C.

The two arcs will intersect at two points. Let's call the upper intersection point F and the lower one G. Now, using a straightedge, draw a straight line through points F, E, and G. This line is perpendicular to AB at E.

Lines, Rays, and Angles

In the geometry, understanding lines, rays, and angles is fundamental.

- **Lines:** A line is a straight one-dimensional figure that extends infinitely in both directions.
  A line passing through points A and B can be denoted as $\overline{AB}$.

- **Rays:** A ray starts at a particular point and goes on infinitely in one direction.
  A ray starting at point A and passing through point B can be denoted as $\overrightarrow{AB}$.

- **Angles:** An angle is formed when two rays meet at a common endpoint.
  An angle formed by rays BA and BC with the vertex at B can be denoted as $\angle ABC$.

- Notice: The sum of angles around a point is $360°$. So, if you know the measure of some angles, you can determine the others using the equation:
  $$\angle A + \angle B + \ldots = 360°$$

- **The Measure of an Angle:** The measure of an angle refers to the amount of rotation required to superimpose one of the two sides of the angle onto the other side. The measure of an angle is symbolized by $m\angle A$ or $m\angle BAC$.

Example:

The diagram shown is not drawn to scale. If $m\angle OMN = x + 5$, $m\angle LMO = 35°$, and $m\angle LMN = 3x - 10$, then find the numerical value of $m\angle LMN$.

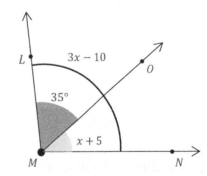

Solution: From the information given and using the properties of angles, we know that angles $m\angle LMN = m\angle LMO + m\angle OMN$. Therefore, solve the equation for x:

$$m\angle LMN = m\angle LMO + m\angle OMN \rightarrow 3x - 10 = 35 + x + 5 \rightarrow 2x = 50 \rightarrow x = 25$$

Now, to find $m\angle LMN$:

$$m\angle LMN = 3x - 10 = 3(25) - 10 = 75 - 10 = 65°$$

Thus, the numerical value of $m\angle LMN$ is $65°$.

bit.ly/3tXIYKG
Find more at

Types of Angles

- Angles, which are formed when two rays meet at a vertex, come in various types based on their measure. Here are the primary types, their definitions, and examples:

- **Acute Angle:** An angle that measures less than 90°.

- **Right Angle:** An angle that measures exactly 90°.

- **Obtuse Angle:** An angle that measures more than 90° but less than 180°.

- **Straight Angle:** An angle that measures exactly 180°.

- **Reflex Angle:** An angle that measures more than 180° but less than 360°.

- **Full Rotation:** An angle that measures exactly 360°.

- **Complementary Angles:** Two angles whose measures add up to 90°.

- **Supplementary Angles:** Two angles whose measures add up to 180°.

Examples:

Example 1. Given an angle that measures 95°, what type of angle is it?

Solution: Since 95° is more than 90° but less than 180°, the angle is an obtuse angle.

Example 2. Consider two rays, $\overrightarrow{DE}$ and $\overrightarrow{DF}$, meeting at point D. If the measure of $\angle EDF$ is 45°, what type of angle is it?

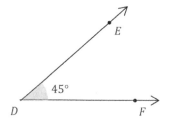

Solution: Since 45° is less than 90°, $\angle EDF$ is an acute angle.

Complementary and Supplementary Angles

- Two angles with a sum of 90 degrees are called complementary angles.

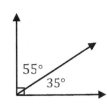

- Two angles with a sum of 180 degrees are Supplementary angles.

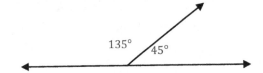

Examples:

Example 1. Find the missing angle.

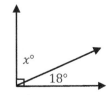

Solution: Notice that the two angles form a right angle. This means that the angles are complementary, and their sum is 90. Then: $18 + x = 90 \rightarrow x = 90° - 18° = 72°$
The missing angle is 72 degrees. $x = 72°$

Example 2. Angles Q and S are supplementary. What is the measure of angle Q if angle S is 35 degrees?

Solution: Q and S are supplementary $\rightarrow Q + S = 180 \rightarrow Q + 35 = 180 \rightarrow$
$$Q = 180 - 35 = 145$$

Example 3. Angles x and y are complementary. What is the measure of angle x if angle y is 16 degrees?

Solution: Angles x and y are complementary $\rightarrow x + y = 90 \rightarrow x + 16 = 90 \rightarrow$
$$x = 90 - 16 = 74$$

Example 4. Find the missing angle.

Solution: The angles are supplementary, and their sum is 180. Then: $67 + x = 180 \rightarrow x = 180° - 67° = 113°$
The missing angle is 113 degrees. $x = 113°$

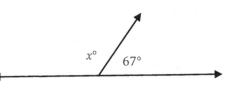

Bisecting an Angle

- Bisecting an angle divides it into two congruent angles, each measuring half of the original angle's measurement. Here's a step-by-step guide to bisecting an angle:

  ▪ **Locate the Vertex:** Consider an angle ∠*ABC* with vertex *B*.

  ▪ **Draw an Arc:** Position the compass point on the vertex *B*. Without specifying a radius (just ensure it's large enough), draw an arc that cuts both rays, *BA* and *BC*. Let these intersection points be *D* (on *BA*) and *E* (on *BC*).

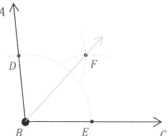

  ▪ **Draw Another Arc:** Without adjusting the compass width, place the compass point on *D* and draw a semi-arc within the angle. Similarly, place the compass point on *E* and draw another semi-arc so that the two arcs intersect. Let this intersection point be *F*.

  ▪ **Draw the Bisector:** Using the straightedge, draw a ray from vertex *B* through point *F*. This ray, labeled *BF*, bisects ∠*ABC* into two congruent angles.

Examples:

Example 1. Given ∠*XYZ* with vertex *Y*, if the angle measures 80°, what will be the measure of the angles formed after bisecting it?

Solution: After bisecting ∠*XYZ*, the two congruent angles formed will each measure half of 80°: $\frac{80°}{2} = 40°$

So, each of the angles will measure 40°.

Example 2. Given angle *ABC* with its bisector *BD*, if the measure of angle *ABD* is 25°, what is the measure of angle *DBC*?

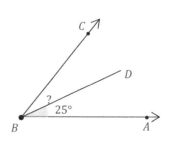

Solution: Given that *BD* bisects angle *ABC*, this means that angle *ABD* (the first half) is equal to angle *DBC* (the second half).

If the measure of angle *ABD* is given as 25°, then the measure of angle *DBC* is also 25° because *BD* bisects angle *ABC*.

Constructing a Triangle Given Its Sides

- Creating a triangle given the lengths of its three sides, often referred to as the SSS (Side-Side-Side) criterion for constructing triangles. Steps to Construct a Triangle Using SSS Criterion:

    - **Draw the Base:** Choose one side as the base. Let's say the side is of length a. Draw a line segment AB of length a using the straightedge.

    - **Construct the Second Side:** Take the second side's length (say, b) on the compass. Place the compass point on B and draw an arc with radius b.

    - **Construct the Third Side:** Similarly, take the third side's length (say, c) on the compass. Without adjusting the compass width, place the compass point on A and draw an arc with radius c. The point where this arc intersects the previous arc is the third vertex of the triangle. Label this point as C.

    - **Complete the Triangle:** Join points A and C, and B and C using the straightedge to form the triangle ABC.

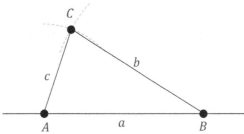

Example:

Construct a triangle with sides measuring $5\ cm$, $6\ cm$, and $7\ cm$.

Solution: Draw a line segment AB of $5\ cm$ (our chosen base).

With the compass set to $6\ cm$ (the second side), draw an arc centered at A.

Similarly, with the compass set to $7\ cm$ (the third side), draw an arc centered at B.

The intersection of these arcs determines point C.

Join A to C and B to C to complete the triangle.

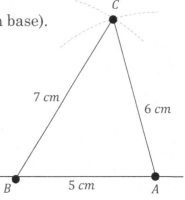

bit.ly/3QtWw8q

Find more at

The Circumscribed Circle

- The circumscribed circle or circumcircle of a polygon is a circle that passes through all the vertices of the polygon.

- Construction of the Circumscribed Circle of a Triangle:

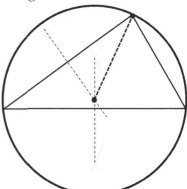

　　Find the Perpendicular Bisectors: For each side of the triangle, find its midpoint. Draw the perpendicular bisector for each side using a compass and straightedge.

- Locate the Circumcenter: The point where all three perpendicular bisectors of a triangle intersect is called the circumcenter. For an acute triangle, the circumcenter lies inside the triangle; for a right triangle, it's on the hypotenuse; and for an obtuse triangle, it's outside the triangle.

- Draw the Circumcircle: Place the compass point on the circumcenter. Adjust the compass width to reach any vertex of the triangle.
Draw a circle that passes through all three vertices of the triangle.

- Properties:

- The circumcenter is equidistant from all three vertices of the triangle. This distance is called the circumradius.
- The circumcenter of a triangle is the center for the circumscribed circle.
- In a triangle, the perpendicular bisectors of the sides are concurrent (they pass through a single point), and this point is the circumcenter.

Example:

Given triangle ABC, after constructing the circumcircle, if the circumradius (distance from circumcenter to any vertex) is 5 cm, what is the length from the circumcenter to vertex A?

Solution: Since the circumradius is the distance from the circumcenter to any vertex of the triangle, the length from the circumcenter to vertex A is also 5 cm.

The Inscribed Circle of a Triangle

- The inscribed circle, or incircle, of a triangle is the largest circle that can fit inside the triangle, touching all three sides.

- Construction of the Incircle of a Triangle:

   - **Construct the Angle Bisectors:** Use a compass and straightedge to bisect the angle.

   - **Determine the Incenter:** The incenter is the point where all three angle bisectors of a triangle intersect.

   - **Find the Inradius:** Using the compass, measure the perpendicular distance from the incenter to any side of the triangle. This distance is the inradius.

   - **Draw the Incircle:** Place the compass point on the incenter and set its width to the inradius. Draw a circle. It will touch all three sides of the triangle.

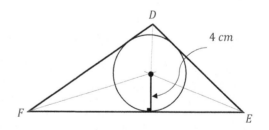

- Properties:

   - The incenter is equidistant from all three sides of the triangle.
   - The incenter is the point of concurrency of the triangle's angle bisectors.
   - The tangents from the incenter to the triangle's sides are of equal lengths.
   - The inradius, when multiplied by the triangle's semiperimeter (half of the perimeter), gives the triangle's area.

Example:

Given triangle DEF, after constructing the incircle, if the inradius is $4\,cm$, and the triangle's perimeter is $36\,cm$, what is the area of triangle DEF?

Solution: Using the property of the inradius:

Area of triangle = inradius × semiperimeter

$$\rightarrow Area = 4\,cm \times \frac{36\,cm}{2} = 4\,cm \times 18\,cm = 72\,cm^2$$

Thus, the area of triangle DEF is $72\,cm^2$.

Inscribing Regular Polygons

- Inscribing a polygon means to draw it inside a circle so that all of its vertices lie on the circumference of the circle. When the polygon is regular (all sides and angles are equal), the task becomes straightforward due to the symmetrical nature of regular polygons.

- General Steps to Inscribe a Regular Polygon in a Circle:

  ▪ **Draw the Circumscribing Circle:** Start by drawing a circle of the desired radius. This will be the circumscribing circle for the polygon.

  ▪ **Divide the Circle:** Calculate the central angle for the polygon using the formula: $Central\ Angle = \frac{360°}{n}$

  where n is the number of sides of the polygon. Using this angle, you can divide the circle into equal parts.

  ▪ **Draw the Polygon:** Start at any point on the circle.

  Use the compass or protractor to mark each subsequent vertex of the polygon by stepping the central angle around the circle.

  Connect the vertices with straight lines using the straightedge to form the inscribed polygon.

Examples:

Draw a Regular hexagon, inside a circle.

Solution: Draw a circle with the compass.

A hexagon has 6 sides, so the central angle is $\frac{360°}{6} = 60°$.

Start at any point on the circle and mark it as the first vertex.

Using a protractor or compass, measure 60° around the circle from the first vertex to locate the second vertex.

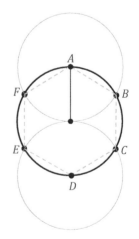

Repeat the process around the circle to find all six vertices. Connect the vertices with straight lines to form the inscribed hexagon.

Chapter 1: Practices

✎ **Classify each statement as true or false.**

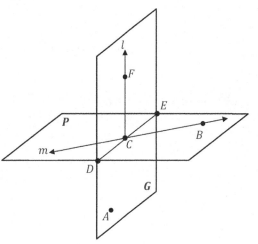

1) $\overline{CF}$ is in plane P._____

2) E is in plane p. _____

3) $B, C,$ and A are coplanar. _____

4) Plane G contains $C, D, E,$ and F. _____

5) Line m intersects $\overline{CF}$ at C. _____

✎ **Find the length of AB.**

6)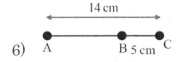

7)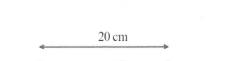

8)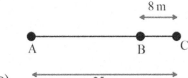

9)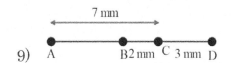

10)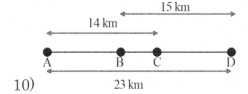

11)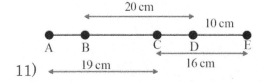

✎ **Points A, B and C are collinear. Point B is between A and C. find the length indicated.**

12) Find AC if $AB = 44$ and $BC = 21$

13) Find AC if $AB = 4$ and $BC = 9$

Effortless
Math
Education

✎ **Points _A_, _B_ and _C_ are collinear. Point _B_ is between _A_ and _C_.**
Solve for _x_.

14) $AC = x + 29$, $AB = -3 + 4x$, and $BC = 23$.

15) $AC = 24$, $BC = x + 4$, and $AB = x + 8$

✎ **Locate the midpoint of each line segment.**

16)    17)

✎ **Solve.**

18) Construct a line segment half as long as the given line segment.

19) Divide the line segment into the 3 equal parts.

✎ **Find the distance between each two points.**

20) -2, 12 22) -14, -3

21) 5, 9 23) 6, -7

24)

25)

✎ **Identify each pair of angles as corresponding, alternate interior, alternate exterior, or consecutive interior and find the measure of each angle indicated.**

26)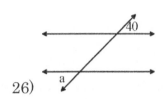

29)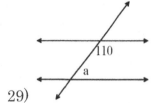

27)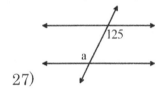

30)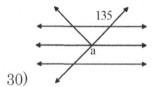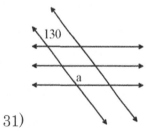

28)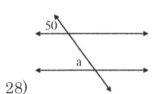

31)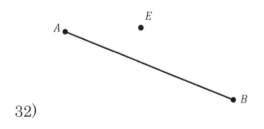

✎ **Draw a perpendicular line from point _E_ on line _AB_.**

32)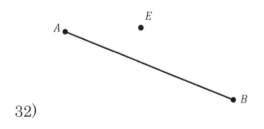

34)

33)

35)

✑ **Find the measure of each angle to the nearest degree.**

36)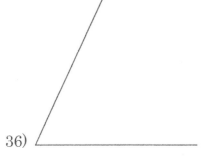

40)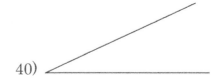

37)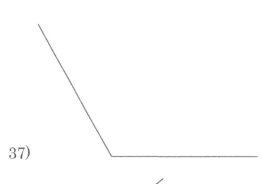

41)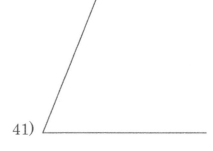

38)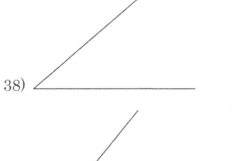

42)

39)

43)

✎ **Classify each angle as acute, obtuse, right, or straight.**

44)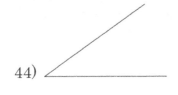

47)

45)

48)

46)

49)

50) 66°   53) 90°   56) 170°

51) 122°   54) 10°   57) 91°

52) 180°   55) 45°   58) 89°

✎ **Name the vertex and sides of each angle.**

59)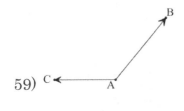

61)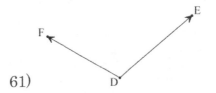

60)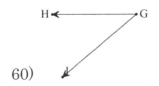

62)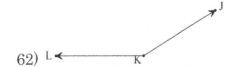

✎ **Draw and label an angle to fit each description.**

63) an actute angle, ∠A

64) a right angle, ∠4

65) an obtuse angle, ∠ABC

66) a straight angle, ∠DEF

✎ **Name all the angles that have _V_ as a vertex.**

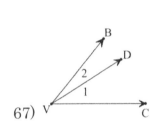

67)

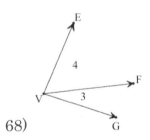

68)

✎ **Draw and label an angle to fit each description.**

69) $m\angle GDF = 35°$

and $m\angle FDE = 70°$

Find $m\angle GDE$

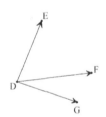

70) Find $m\angle KHJ$

if $m\angle KHI = 145°$

and $m\angle JHI = 45°$

71) $m\angle OLN = 50°$

and $m\angle OLM = 180°$

Find $m\angle NLM$

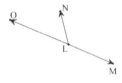

72) Find $m\angle RPQ$

if $m\angle SPR = 90°$

and $m\angle SPQ = 120°$

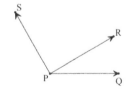

Effortless
Math
Education

✎ **Construct the bisector of each angle.**

73)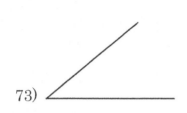

74)

75)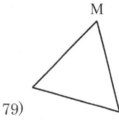

76)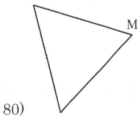

✎ **Construct the bisector of each angle.**

77)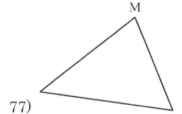
M

78)
M

79)
M

80)
M

✎ **Construct a triangle whose sides are half as long as the sides of the given triangle.**

81)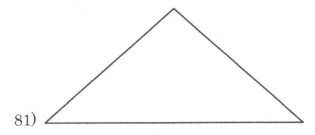

Effortless Math Education

Construct an isosceles triangle according to the given lengths.

82) Base: —————————

Side: —————————

83) Base: ——————————

Altitude: ——————————

Construct a right triangle given the hypotenuse and a leg.

84) Hypotenuse: —————————————

Leg: ——————————

Locate the circumcenter of each triangle.

85) 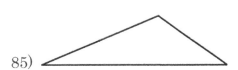   86)

Circumscribe a circle about each triangle.

87) 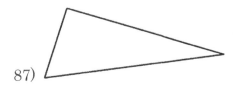   88)

✎ **Find the radius of the inscribed circle in the triangle. Round your answer to nearest tenth.**

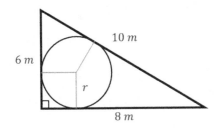

89)

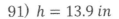

91) $h = 13.9\ in$

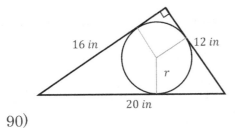

90)

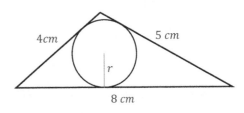

92) Area $= 8.2\ cm^2$

✎ **Draw the given Regular polygon, inside a circle with compass.**

93) Heptagon

94) Pentagon

95) Octagon

Effortless
Math
Education

Chapter 1: Answers

1) False

2) True

3) False

4) True

5) True

6) 9 *cm*

7) 7 *cm*

8) 17 *m*

9) 2 *mm*

10) 8 *km*

11) 5 *cm*

12) 63

13) 13

14) 3

15) 6

16)

17)

18) —————— ——————

19) —————— —————— ——————

20) 14

21) 4

22) 11

23) 13

24) 6

25) 15

26) Alternate exterior, $a = 40°$

27) Alternate interior, $a = 125°$

28) Corresponding, $a = 50°$

29) Consecutive interior, $a = 70°$

30) Alternate exterior, $a = 135°$

31) Corresponding, $a = 130°$

32)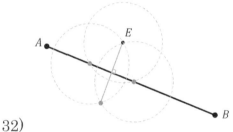

33)

34)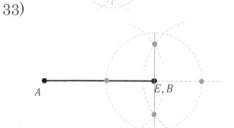

35)

36) 65°

37) 120°

38) 40°

39) 50°

40) 24°

41) 68°

42) 10°

43) 150°

44) Acute

45) Obtuse

46) Acute

47) Straight

48) Acute

49) Obtuse

50) Acute

51) Obtuse

52) Straight

53) Right

54) Acute

55) Acute

56) Obtuse

57) Obtuse

58) Acute

59) Vertex: point A

   Sides: $\overrightarrow{AB}, \overrightarrow{AC}$

60) Vertex: point G

   Sides: $\overrightarrow{GH}, \overrightarrow{GI}$

61) Vertex: point D

   Sides: $\overrightarrow{DF}, \overrightarrow{DE}$

62) Vertex: point K

   Sides: $\overrightarrow{KL}, \overrightarrow{KJ}$

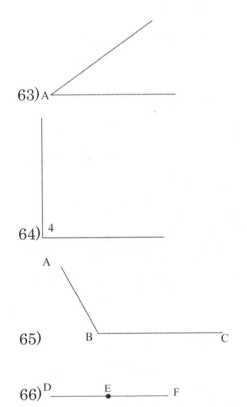

63) A

64) 4

65)

66)

67) $\angle BVD, \angle BVC, \angle DVC$

68) $\angle EVF, \angle EVG, \angle FVG$

69) 105°

70) 100°

71) 130°

72) 30°

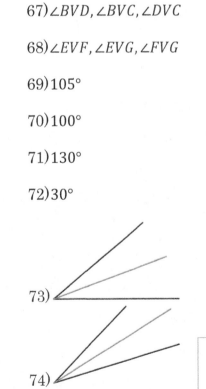

73)

74)

Effortless
Math
Education

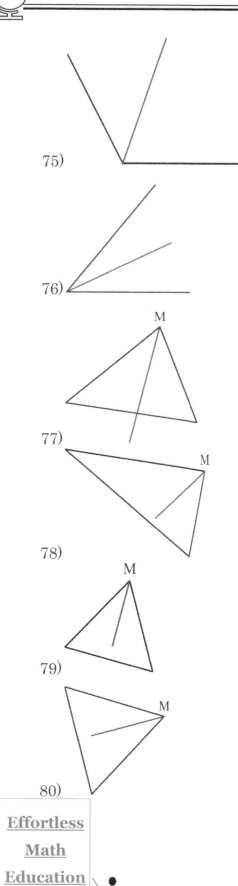

75)

76)

77)

78)

79)

80)

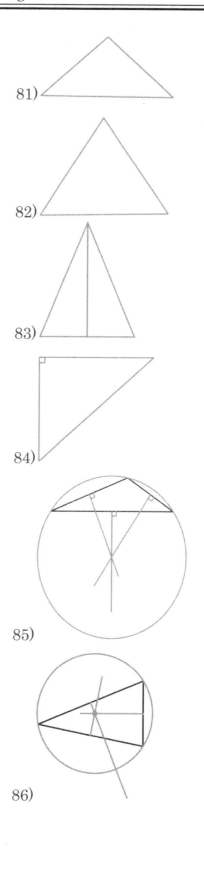

81)

82)

83)

84)

85)

86)

**Effortless
Math
Education**

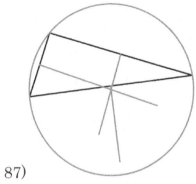

87)

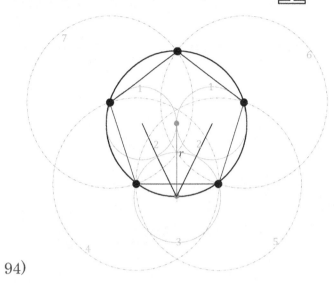

94)

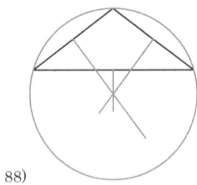

88)

89) $r = 2\ m$

90) $r = 4\ in$

91) $r \approx 4.6\ in$

92) $r \approx 0.96\ cm$

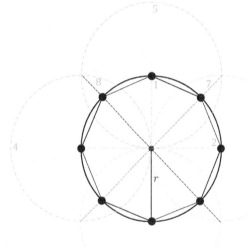

95)

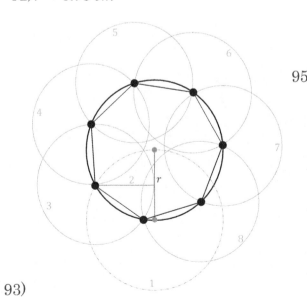

93)

CHAPTER

2 Reasoning and Proofs

Math topics that you'll learn in this chapter:

- ☑ Conjectures and Counterexamples
- ☑ Inductive Reasoning from Patterns
- ☑ Conditional Statements
- ☑ Logic and Truth Tables
- ☑ Converse, Inverse, and Contrapositive
- ☑ Biconditionals and Definitions
- ☑ Deductive Reasoning
- ☑ Properties of Equality and Congruence
- ☑ Two Column Proofs
- ☑ Proving Angles Congruent

29

Conjectures and Counterexamples

- **Conjecture:** A conjecture is an unproven statement or proposition that appears to be true based on preliminary or limited evidence. In mathematics, it's essentially an educated guess or hypothesis about a mathematical rule or theorem.

- **Counterexample:** A counterexample is an example that disproves a statement or proposition. If even one counterexample exists for a conjecture, then the conjecture is proven to be false.

- **Conjecture Creation:** Often, when exploring mathematical patterns or working through problems, mathematicians might observe a pattern or trend. This observation might lead them to make a conjecture about a general rule or theorem.

- **Verifying with Counterexamples:** Once a conjecture is made, mathematicians will try to either prove it using established mathematical theorems or disprove it by finding a counterexample. If a single counterexample is found, the conjecture is immediately disproven.

- **Notice:** The existence of even a single counterexample is enough to disprove a conjecture.

- **Notice:** Proving a conjecture requires more rigorous mathematical exploration and cannot be done merely by providing numerous examples that support the conjecture.

Examples:

Determine if these conjectures are true or if there are counterexamples.

Example 1. Conjecture: All even numbers are divisible by 2.

Solution: This is actually a true statement, and no counterexample can be found.

Example 2. Conjecture: All prime numbers are odd.

Solution: Counterexample 2 is a prime number, but it is even. This single counterexample disproves the conjecture.

Example 3. Conjecture: The sum of two odd numbers is always even.

Solution: This statement holds true, and no counterexamples exist for this conjecture.

Inductive Reasoning from Patterns

- Inductive reasoning is a type of reasoning where general conclusions are drawn from specific observations. The conclusion drawn from inductive reasoning might be probable but not necessarily certain.

- **Observing Patterns:** The first step in inductive reasoning is to observe and identify patterns or trends in specific cases or sets of data.

- **Making Generalizations:** Once a pattern is identified, a general statement or hypothesis is formed based on those patterns. This general statement applies beyond the initially observed cases.

- **Limitations:** It's important to note that inductive reasoning doesn't guarantee the conclusion's correctness. A conclusion drawn using induction is based on observed evidence, but there might always be an exception or a scenario where the conclusion doesn't hold.

- **Application in Mathematics:** Inductive reasoning is often used in mathematics, especially when observing patterns in numbers, sequences, or geometric shapes.

  - **Number Patterns:** Observation is $2, 4, 6, 8, \ldots$. Inductive reasoning is the sequence is increasing by 2; the next number is likely 10.

  - **Geometric Patterns:** Observation is the angles of any triangle you measure sum up to $180°$. Inductive reasoning is the angles in all triangles sum up to $180°$.

- **Notice:** While inductive reasoning starts with specifics and makes generalizations, deductive reasoning starts with a general statement or hypothesis and examines the possibilities to reach a specific, logical conclusion.

- **Notice:** It's essential to verify conclusions drawn from inductive reasoning. Just because a pattern exists doesn't mean it's universally true.

Examples:

Example 1. Draw a conclusion using inductive reasoning:

Every time you drop a pen, it falls to the ground.

Solution: Inductive Reasoning: Objects fall to the ground when dropped.

Example 2. Use the pattern below to answer the questions.

a) Draw the next figure in the pattern.

b) How does the number of dots in each shape relate to the figure number?

c) Use part b to determine a formula for the *nth* figure.

Solution: Let's address each part:

a) Shape5: Given the current pattern, the next figure would have 8 dots.

b) From the pattern, we can observe that each subsequent figure has one more dot than the previous figure. If you align this with the figure number:

Shape1 (figure number 1) has $1 + 3 = 4$ dots.

Shape2 (figure number 2) has $2 + 3 = 5$ dots.

Shape3 (figure number 3) has $3 + 3 = 6$ dots. And so on...

So, each shape's number of dots is the figure number plus 3.

c) Use part b to determine a formula for the nth figure.

Based on the pattern observed in part b, the formula for the nth figure in terms of the number of dots is:

$$Dots = n + 3$$

Thus, for any given figure number '*n*', you can determine the number of dots it has by adding 3 to that figure number.

Conditional Statements

- A conditional statement, often referred to as an "if-then" statement, is a statement that can be written in the form "if p, then q," where p is a hypothesis and q is a conclusion.

  - **Hypothesis:** The "if" part of the statement. It's denoted as p.

  - **Conclusion:** The "then" part of the statement. It's denoted as q.

- **Symbolic Representation:** A conditional statement can be represented symbolically as: $p \to q$

  Where, p is Hypothesis and q is Conclusion.

- **Notice:** The conditional statement $p \to q$ is false only when p is true and q is false. In all other cases, it is true.

p	q	$p \to q$
True	True	True
True	False	False
False	True	True
False	False	True

Examples:

Determine the hypothesis and conclusion in the following statements.

Example 1. If a number is even, then it is divisible by 2.

Solution: Hypothesis: A number is even.
Conclusion: It is divisible by 2.

Example 2. If a shape has four sides, then it is a quadrilateral.

Solution: Hypothesis: a shape has four sides.
Conclusion: it is a quadrilateral.
So, the statement is saying: based on the condition (or hypothesis) that a shape has four sides, we can conclude that the shape is a quadrilateral.

Example 3. If $2 + 2 = 5$, then pigs can fly.

Solution: Hypothesis: $2 + 2 = 5$.
Conclusion: pigs can fly.
The statement $2 + 2 = 5$ is clearly false. The statement "pigs can fly" is also false under normal circumstances. Therefore, the statement "If $2 + 2 = 5$, then pigs can fly" is true based on the principles of classical logic, even though both its parts are false.

bit.ly/46WzuOe

Find more at

Logic and Truth Tables

- **Truth tables:** Truth tables are tabular representations that list the possible truth values of logical expressions based on their compound statements.

- **Logic:** It deals with statements that are either true or false and the logical connections between them.

- **Basic Logical Connectives:**

  - **Conjunction (AND):** This is represented by the symbol (∧). A conjunction is true only when both of its components are true.

p	q	$p \wedge q$
True	True	True
True	False	False
False	True	False
False	False	False

  - **Disjunction (OR):** Represented by the symbol (∨). A disjunction is true when at least one of its components is true.

p	q	$p \vee q$
True	True	True
True	False	True
False	True	True
False	False	False

  - **Negation (NOT):** Represented by the symbol (¬). It flips the truth value of a statement.

p	$\neg p$
True	False
False	True

  - **Conditional (IMPLIES):** Represented by (→). It's an "if-then" statement.

p	q	$p \to q$
True	True	True
True	False	False
False	True	True
False	False	True

  - **Biconditional (IF AND ONLY IF):** Represented by (↔). It's true when both its components have the same truth value.

p	q	$p \leftrightarrow q$
True	True	True
True	False	False
False	True	False
False	False	True

- **Notice:** the symbol of therefore is (∴).

Examples:

Example 1. Create a truth table for the statement $(p \lor \neg q)$.

Solution: Truth table for $p \lor \neg q$

p	q	$\neg q$	$p \lor \neg q$
T	T	F	T
T	F	T	T
F	T	F	F
F	F	T	T

Example 2. Determine the truth value of the statement $(\neg p \land q)$ when p is false and q is true.

Solution: If p is false and q is true, then $\neg p$ would be true.

So, $\neg p \land q = \text{True} \land \text{True} = \text{True}$

Example 3. Create a truth table for the compound statement $(p \to q) \land (q \to p)$.

Solution: Truth table for $(p \to q) \land (q \to p)$

For $q \to p$ (if q then p):

p	q	$p \to q$
T	T	T
T	F	F
F	T	T
F	F	T

For $p \to q$ (if p then q):

p	q	$q \to p$
T	T	T
T	F	T
F	T	F
F	F	T

Finally, for $(p \to q) \land (q \to p)$:

$p \to q$	$q \to p$	$(p \to q) \land (q \to p)$
T	T	T
F	T	F
T	F	F
T	T	T

bit.ly/3QH62WS

Find more at

Converse, Inverse, and Contrapositive

- A conditional statement is often written in the form "if p, then q" and is denoted as ($p \rightarrow q$). Here, p is the hypothesis or premise, and q is the conclusion. To check whether the statement is true or false, we have subsequent parts of a conditional statement. They are:

    - **Converse:** The statement formed by swapping the hypothesis and the conclusion. The converse of the statement ($p \rightarrow q$) is ($q \rightarrow p$).

    - **Inverse:** The statement formed by negating both the hypothesis and the conclusion. The inverse of the statement ($p \rightarrow q$) is ($\neg p \rightarrow \neg q$).

    - **Contrapositive:** The statement formed by negating and swapping the hypothesis and the conclusion. The contrapositive of the statement ($p \rightarrow q$) is ($\neg q \rightarrow \neg p$).

- **Properties:**

    - If a conditional statement is true, its contrapositive is also true.

    - The converse and inverse of a conditional statement may not necessarily have the same truth value as the original statement.

    - If a conditional statement is true and its converse is true, then it can be combined as a biconditional statement, denoted as ($p \leftrightarrow q$), which means p if and only if q.

Example:

write subsequent parts of the given conditional statement. then Analyze it.

"If it is raining, then the ground is wet."

Solution:

Converse: "If the ground is wet, then it is raining."
Inverse: "If it is not raining, then the ground is not wet."
Contrapositive: "If the ground is not wet, then it is not raining."

Analysis: From the given statement, we cannot always conclude the converse to be true because there could be other reasons for the ground to be wet (e.g., someone watered the plants). However, the contrapositive is true. If we know the ground is not wet, we can conclude that it is not raining.

bit.ly/46WzuOe

Biconditionals and Definitions

- A biconditional statement is a statement that contains the phrase "if and only if," often abbreviated as "iff." Symbolically, it is represented as $p \leftrightarrow q$. For the biconditional to be true, both parts (the "if" part and the "only if" part) must be true or both must be false.

- **Properties:**

  ▪ A biconditional statement is true when both the conditional statement and its converse are true.

  ▪ In terms of truth values, $p \leftrightarrow q$ is true if both p and q are true or both p and q are false. Otherwise, it's false.

  ▪ Biconditionals are often used to write definitions in mathematics because definitions are true in both directions.

Examples:

Write the biconditional for the following statement:

Example 1. statement: "A shape is a square if and only if it has four equal sides."

Solution: Here, the "if" part means: If a shape is a square, then it has four equal sides.

The "only if" part means: If a shape has four equal sides, then it is a square.

Example 2. Statement: "Two angles are complementary if and only if their measures add up to 90°."

Solution: The two directions of this statement are:

If two angles are complementary, their measures add up to 90°.

If the measures of two angles add up to 90°, they are complementary.

bit.ly/49gfsQv

Find more at

Deductive Reasoning

- Deductive reasoning is a method of reasoning from one or more statements (premises) to reach a logically certain conclusion. Deductive reasoning goes from the general to the specific. It's also known as "top-down" reasoning.

- **Properties:**

  ▪ Deductive reasoning is based on premises and if the premises are true, then the reasoning will be valid.

  ▪ The conclusion reached is logically certain, which means if the premises are true, the conclusion cannot be false.

  ▪ Deductive reasoning is commonly used in formal logic and mathematics.

- While deductive reasoning starts with a general statement and examines the possibilities to reach a specific, logical conclusion, inductive reasoning starts with specific observations and measures, and then makes generalizations based on that, often leading to hypotheses or theories.

Examples:

Example 1. Identify the conclusions:

Premise 1: The sum of the angles in a triangle is 180°.

Premise 2: In triangle ABC, angles A and B measure 60° each.

Solution: The conclusion is: Angle C in triangle ABC measures 60°.

Example 2. Identify the conclusions:

Premise 1: If it rains, then the ground will be wet.

Premise 2: It rained.

Solution: this is an if-Then Statements, and the conclusion is: The ground is wet.

bit.ly/40jG6DO
Find more at

Properties of Equality and Congruence

- Equality is a relation that holds between two values when they are the same in value.

  ▪ Reflexive Property of Equality: For any number (a), $(a = a)$.

  ▪ Symmetric Property of Equality: If $(a = b)$, then $(b = a)$.

  ▪ Transitive Property of Equality: If $(a = b)$ and $(b = c)$, then $(a = c)$.

  ▪ Substitution Property of Equality: If $(a = b)$, then b can be used in place of a and vice versa.

  ▪ Addition Property of Equality: If $(a = b)$, then $(a + c = b + c)$ for any number (c).

  ▪ Subtraction Property of Equality: If $(a = b)$, then $(a - c = b - c)$ for any number (c).

  ▪ Multiplication Property of Equality: If $(a = b)$, then $(ac = bc)$ for any number (c).

  ▪ Division Property of Equality: If $(a = b)$ and $(c \neq 0)$, then $(\frac{a}{c} = \frac{b}{c})$.

  ▪ Distributive Property: $a(b + c) = ab + ac$

- In geometry, two figures or objects are congruent if they have the same shape and size, or if one has the same shape and size as the mirror image of the other.

  ▪ Reflexive Property of Congruence: A geometric figure is congruent to itself. For example, if $(\angle A)$ is an angle, then $(\angle A \cong \angle A)$.

  ▪ Symmetric Property of Congruence: If $(\angle A \cong \angle B)$, then $(\angle B \cong \angle A)$.

  ▪ Transitive Property of Congruence: If $(\angle A \cong \angle B)$ and $(\angle B \cong \angle C)$, then $(\angle A \cong \angle C)$.

  ▪ Congruence of Segments: Two-line segments are congruent if they have the same length.

  ▪ Congruence of Angles: Two angles are congruent if they have the same measure.

Examples:

Example 1. If $(x = 5)$ and $(5 = y)$, which property of equality allows us to deduce $(x = y)$?

Solution: The property of equality that allows this deduction is the Transitive Property of Equality.

Example 2. Given $\triangle ABC$ and $\triangle DEF$ such that $\overline{AB} \cong \overline{DE}$ and $\overline{BC} \cong \overline{EF}$, if $\overline{AC} \cong \overline{DF}$, which property helps us conclude $\triangle ABC \cong \triangle DEF$?

Solution: The property that helps us conclude $\triangle ABC \cong \triangle DEF$ given the conditions is the Side-Side-Side (SSS) Postulate for triangle congruence.

Example 3. Identify which property is being used: "If $2x + 3 = 7$ and $2x = 4$, then $4 + 3 = 7$".

Solution: The property being used here is the Substitution Property of Equality.

Two Column Proofs

- A two-column proof is a method used primarily in geometry to demonstrate the logical steps in deducing a conclusion from a given set of premises.

- In this type of proof, each justification step is paired with a statement in a two-column format.

  - The left column contains statements.

  - The right column contains corresponding reasons or justifications.

- Remember, the goal of a two-column proof is to lay out a clear logical sequence from given information to the final conclusion, using definitions, postulates, and previously proven theorems.

Example:

Given: $AB \parallel CD$ and $\angle BE \cong \angle DCE$

Prove: $\angle BEC$ is a straight angle (measures 180°).

Solution: Two-Column Proof:

Statements	Reasons
1. $AB \parallel CD$	1. Given
2. $\angle BE \cong \angle DCE$	2. Given
3. $\angle ABE$ and $\angle DCE$ are alternate interior angles.	3. Definition of alternate interior angles.
4. Alternate interior angles are congruent when lines are parallel.	4. Theorem on alternate interior angles.
5. $\angle ABE + \angle BEC = 180°$	5. Linear pair postulate
6. $\angle DCE + \angle BEC = 180°$	6. Linear pair postulate
7. $\angle BEC$ is a straight angle.	7. Definition of a straight angle.

bit.ly/3Qn2lUV

Find more at

Proving Angles Congruent

In geometry, when we want to prove that angles are congruent, we often rely on certain postulates, properties, or theorems. Here are some of the most commonly used methods to prove angles congruent:

- **Angle Congruence Postulate:** If two angles have the same measure, they are congruent.

- **Vertical Angles Theorem:** Vertical angles (angles formed by intersecting lines) are always congruent.

- **Adjacent Angles:** Angles that share a common vertex and side but do not share any interior points are called adjacent angles. They might or might not be congruent, but sometimes we can use their relationship to other angles to prove congruence.

- **Complementary and Supplementary Angles:** If two angles are complementary to the same angle (or to congruent angles), then the two angles are congruent.

- **Alternate Interior Angles:** When two lines are cut by a transversal, the pairs of alternate interior angles are congruent if the two lines are parallel.

- **Alternate Exterior Angles:** When two lines are cut by a transversal, the pairs of alternate exterior angles are congruent if the two lines are parallel.

- **Corresponding Angles:** When two lines are cut by a transversal, the pairs of corresponding angles are congruent if the two lines are parallel.

- **Angles Formed by Perpendicular Lines:** If two lines are perpendicular, they form four right angles, which are all congruent.

Example:

Given: Line l is parallel to line m, and both are cut by a transversal t.

Prove:$\angle 1$ is congruent to $\angle 5$

(Assuming these are corresponding angles formed by the transversal on lines l and m).

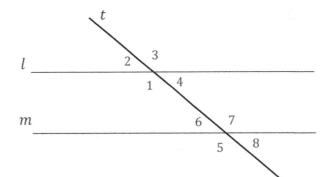

Solution: Two-Column Proof:

Statements	Reasons
1. Line $l \parallel m$	1. Given
2. t is a transversal of l and m	2. By definition of a transversal
3. $\angle 1$ and $\angle 5$ are corresponding angles	3. Definition of corresponding angles
4. $\angle 1 \cong \angle 5$	4. Corresponding angles are congruent if the lines are parallel

Chapter 2: Practices

🖎 Determine if these conjectures are true or if there are counterexamples.

1) The square of any integer is always positive.

2) The sum of two negative integers is always negative.

3) The product of two negative numbers is positive.

4) All numbers divisible by 6 are also divisible by 3.

5) Every triangle has at least two acute angles.

6) If n is an integer, then $n^2 > n$.

7) All numbers that end in 1 are prime numbers.

8) Any three points that are coplanar are also collinear.

9) All girls like ice cream.

10) All high school students are in choir.

11) For any angle, there exists a complementary angle.

12) All teenagers can drive.

🖎 Draw conclusions using inductive reasoning.

13) The first few terms of a sequence are $5, 10, 15, 20, \ldots$

14) In a game of dice, rolling a 6 has occurred more frequently than any other number in the las t 10 rolls.

✎ Using Inductive Reasoning.

15) A dot pattern is shown below. How many dots would there be in the 4th figure? draw the 6th figure?

16) How many circles would be in the 9th figure?

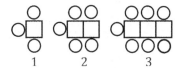

17) Look at the pattern $7, 12, 17, 22, 27, \dots$

What is the 19th term in the pattern?

18) Look at the pattern: $-1, 3, -9, 27, -81, \dots$

What is the next term in the pattern? The 10th term? Make a rule for the nth term.

✎ Identify the hypothesis and conclusion of each conditional.

19) If you can see the sun, then it is day.

Hypothesis: ....

Conclusion: ....

20) If two lines are perpendicular, then they form right angle.

Hypothesis: ....

Conclusion: ....

21) If $m\angle A = 90$, then $m\angle A$ is a right angle.

Hypothesis: ....

Conclusion: ....

22) If $4x - 2 = x + 1$, then: $x = 1$.

Hypothesis: ....

Conclusion: ....

 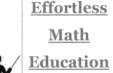

Effortless
Math
Education

Write a conditional statement from each of the following.

23) A tricycle has three wheels.   24) All birds have two wings

For each conditional, write the converse and a biconditional statement.

25) Conditional: If it is the second Sunday in May, then it is Mother's day.

   Converse: ....

   Biconditional: ....

26) Conditional: If a figure has 8 sides, then it is an octagon.

   Converse: ....

   Biconditional: ....

Write a truth table for the following variables.

27) $(p \wedge q) \vee r$ 30) $(p \vee q) \vee \neg r$

28) $p \vee (\neg q \vee r)$ 31) $(\neg p \vee \neg q) \wedge r$

29) $p \wedge (q \vee \neg r)$ 32) $(\neg p \wedge \neg q) \wedge r$

Is the following a valid argument? If so, what law is being used? (Hint: Statements could be out of order).

33) $p \rightarrow q, r \rightarrow p, \therefore r \rightarrow q$ 35) $p \rightarrow r, \neg r, \therefore \neg p$

34) $p \rightarrow q, q \rightarrow r, \therefore p \rightarrow r$ 36) $r \rightarrow q, p \rightarrow r, \therefore q \rightarrow p$

✍ **Determine its converse, inverse, and contrapositive, and if the statements are true or false. Then, if they are false, find a counterexample.**

37) If a shape is a square, then it has four equal sides.

38) If I am at Disneyland, then I am in California.

39) If two lines intersect, then they intersect at exactly one point.

40) If two sides of a triangle are congruent, then the angles opposite those sides are also congruent.

✍ **Determine the two true conditional statements from the given biconditional statements.**

41) A whole number is prime if and only if it has exactly two distinct factors.

42) Points are collinear if and only if there is a line that contains the points.

43) $5x = 15$ if and only if $x = 3$.

✍ **Solve.**

44) Write the biconditional for the following statement: A shape is a rectangle if it has four right angles.

45) Identify the two conditional statements embedded in this biconditional: A polygon is regular if and only if all its sides and angles are congruent.

46) Write a definition using a biconditional for the term "odd number."

✍ **Solve.**

47) What is the relationships between **AD** and **FC**, if **FE = AB** and **ED = BC**.

Effortless

Math

Education

Decide whether the following syllogisms are true or false.

48) All humans are mammals.

All mammals are warm-blooded.

All humans are warm-blooded.

49) All even numbers are divisible by 2.

238 is an even number.

238 is divisible by 2.

50) All kangaroos have two legs.

All humans are two-legged.

All kangaroos are humans.

51) If $3A = B + 2$

And $B = 7$,

Then $A = 3$

Mark "√" in the grid as each added piece of information helps you match the numbers with the people they describe.

52) There are four pencil cases on a table. One pencil case has 12 pencils, one pencil case has 16 pencils, one pencil case has 6 pencils and the other pencil case has 32 pencils.

a) Jack has less pencils than Sarah.

b) Jacob has more pencils than Sarah.

c) David has the most number of pencils.

****	6	12	16	32
Sarah				
Jack				
Jacob				
David				

Use the given property or properties of equality to fill in the blank. a, b, and c are real number.

53) Symmetric: If $a + b = b + c$, then $c + b =$ ____.

54) Transitive: If $XY = 6$ and $XY = ZW$, then $ZW =$ ____.

55) Substitution: If $a = b - 5$ and $a = c + 3$, then $b - 5 =$ ____.

56) Distributive: If $4(2a + 3) = b$, then $b =$ ____.

✍ Solve.

57) Given points O, P, and Q and $OP = 7$, $PQ = 7$, and $OQ = 12$. Are the three points collinear? Is P the midpoint?

58) If $m\angle RST = 60°$ and $m\angle RST + m\angle UVW = 180°$, explain how $\angle UVW$ must be an obtuse angle.

59) Identify which property is being used: "If $2x + 3 = 7$ and $2x = 4$, then $4 + 3 = 7$".

60) Given $\triangle ABC$ and $\triangle DEF$ such that $AB \cong DE$ and $BC \cong EF$, if $AC \cong DF$, which property helps us conclude $\triangle ABC \cong \triangle DEF$?

61) If $x = 5$ and $5 = y$, which property of equality allows us to deduce $x = y$?

✍ Prove it.

62) Given vertices A, B and C form a triangle. Write a proof to show that A, B and C determine a plane.

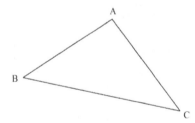

63) Given that D is the midpoint of $\overline{BC}$ and $\angle L \cong \angle B$. Write a proof to show that $\overline{LD} \cong \overline{DC}$.

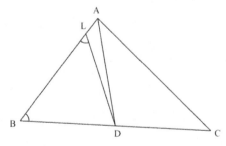

64) Given that B is the midpoint of $\overline{AC}$, D is the midpoint of $\overline{CE}$, and $\overline{AB} = \overline{DE}$. Write a proof to show that $AE = 4AB$.

✎ **Solve.**

65) If **A**, **B**, **C**, **D** and **E** are points on a line, in the given order, and

AB = DE, prove **AD = BE**

66) Given: $u \perp v$ and $\angle \alpha \cong \angle \beta$ and $\angle \theta \cong \angle \lambda$

Prove: $\angle \theta = \angle \gamma + \angle \delta$

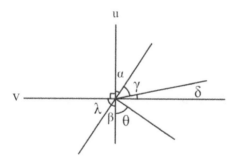

67) Given: $\angle a$ and $\angle b$ are right angles and $m\angle c = 40°$

Prove: $m\angle a + m\angle d + m\angle c = 270°$

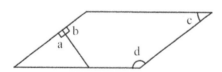

68) Given: $m\angle BOD = 90°$ and $m\angle COD = 35°$ and $m\angle AOB = 40°$

Prove: $m\angle FOE + m\angle BOC = 105°$

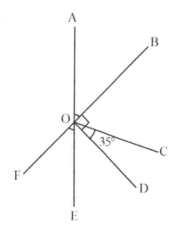

Chapter 2: Answers

1) Counterexample: The square of 0 is $0^2 = 0$, which is not positive.

2) This statement is true. Any combination of two negative integers will always result in a negative sum. Hence, there isn't a counterexample for this claim.

3) This statement is true. When you multiply two negative numbers, the product is always positive. For example, $(-2) \times (-3) = 6$. Therefore, no counterexample can be provided for this claim.

4) This statement is true. Any number divisible by 6 is also divisible by both its prime factors: 2 and 3. So, there isn't a counterexample for this statement.

5) This statement is true. all triangles have at least two acute angles. Acute angles are angles that measure less than 90°, while obtuse angles measure greater than 90°.

6) Counterexample: $n = 1$. Here, $1^2 = 1$, which means n^2 is not greater than n.

7) Counterexample: 91 ends in 1 but is not prime since it's divisible by 7 and 13.

8) Counterexample: Imagine three vertices of a triangle. They are all in the same plane (coplanar) but are not on a single straight line (collinear).

9) Counterexample: Sarah is a girl who is lactose intolerant and dislikes the taste of all ice creams, even lactose-free ones.

10) Counterexample: John is a high school student who is only involved in the chess club and not in the choir.

11) Counterexample: A 120° angle. Complementary angles add up to 90°, so, a 120° angle doesn't have a complementary angle.

Effortless Math Education

12) Counterexample: In many countries, the legal driving age is 18, so a 16-year-old teenager in those countries cannot legally drive.

13) Inductive Reasoning Conclusion: The sequence seems to be increasing by 5 each time. Based on this observed pattern, the next term is likely to be 25.

14) Inductive Reasoning Conclusion: While dice are designed to give random results, you might infer that there seems to be a trend of rolling 6s more frequently in this specific set of rolls. However, this doesn't necessarily mean a 6 will come up in the next roll; statistically, each roll should be independent and have an equal chance of landing on any face.

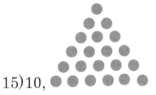

15) 10,   17) 97

16) 19   18) 243, 19,683, $-1(-3)^{n-1}$

19) Hypothesis: You can see the sun

Conclusion: It is day

20) Hypothesis: Two lines are perpendicular

Conclusion: Then they form right angle

21) Hypothesis: Z is an odd number

Conclusion: Z is not divisible by 2

22) Hypothesis: You touch the hot source

Conclusion: Your hands burn

23) If it is a tricycle, then it has three wheels.

24) If they are birds, then they have two wings.

25) Converse: If it is Mother's Day, then it is the second Sunday in May.

Biconditional: It is the second Sunday in May if and only if it is Mother's Day.

26) Converse: If a figure is octagon, then it has 8 sides.

Biconditional: A figure has 8 sides if and only if it is an octagon.

27)   For: $(p \land q) \lor r$

p	q	r	$p \land q$	$(p \land q) \lor r$
T	T	T	T	T
T	T	F	T	T
T	F	T	F	T
T	F	F	F	F
F	T	T	F	T
F	T	F	F	F
F	F	T	F	T
F	F	F	F	F

The truth table covers all possible combinations of truth values for p, q, and r.

28)   For: $p \lor (\neg q \lor r)$

p	q	r	$\neg q$	$\neg q \lor r$	$p \lor (\neg q \lor r)$
T	T	T	F	T	T
T	T	F	F	F	T
T	F	T	T	T	T
T	F	F	T	T	T
F	T	T	F	T	T
F	T	F	F	F	F
F	F	T	T	T	T
F	F	F	T	T	T

The truth table covers all possible combinations of truth values for p, q, and r.

Effortless
Math
Education

29)   For: $p \wedge (q \vee \neg r)$

p	q	r	$\neg r$	$q \vee \neg r$	$p \wedge (q \vee \neg r)$
T	T	T	F	T	T
T	T	F	T	T	T
T	F	T	F	F	F
T	F	F	T	T	T
F	T	T	F	T	F
F	T	F	T	T	F
F	F	T	F	F	F
F	F	F	T	T	F

The truth table covers all possible combinations of truth values for p, q, and r.

30)   For: $(p \vee q) \vee \neg r$

p	q	r	$\neg r$	$p \vee q$	$(p \vee q) \vee \neg r$
T	T	T	F	T	T
T	T	F	T	T	T
T	F	T	F	T	T
T	F	F	T	T	T
F	T	T	F	T	T
F	T	F	T	T	T
F	F	T	F	F	F
F	F	F	T	F	T

The truth table covers all possible combinations of truth values for p, q, and r.

31)   For: $(\neg p \vee \neg q) \wedge r$

p	q	r	$\neg p$	$\neg q$	$\neg p \vee \neg q$	$(\neg p \vee \neg q) \wedge r$
T	T	T	F	F	F	F
T	T	F	F	F	F	F
T	F	T	F	T	T	T
T	F	F	F	T	T	F
F	T	T	T	F	T	T
F	T	F	T	F	T	F
F	F	T	T	T	T	T
F	F	F	T	T	T	F

The truth table covers all possible combinations of truth values for p, q, and r.

32)   For: $(\neg p \wedge \neg q) \wedge r$

p	q	r	$\neg p$	$\neg q$	$\neg p \wedge \neg q$	$(\neg p \wedge \neg q) \wedge r$
T	T	T	F	F	F	F
T	T	F	F	F	F	F
T	F	T	F	T	F	F
T	F	F	F	T	F	F
F	T	T	T	F	F	F
F	T	F	T	F	F	F
F	F	T	T	T	T	T
F	F	F	T	T	T	F

The truth table covers all possible combinations of truth values for p, q, and r.

33) This is a valid argument. If p implies q and r implies p, then r implies q.

34) This is a valid argument. If p implies q and q implies r, then p implies r.

35) This is a valid argument. If p implies r and r is not true, then p must not be true either.

36) This argument is Not valid. The given premises don't support the conclusion. The conclusion $q \rightarrow p$ isn't necessarily true based on the premises provided.

Effortless
Math
Education

37) This statement is true.

Converse: If a shape has four equal sides, then it is a square. (False: A rhombus has four equal sides but is not necessarily a square)

Inverse: If a shape is not a square, then it does not have four equal sides. (True).

Contrapositive: If a shape does not have four equal sides, then it is not a square. (True).

38) This statement Not necessarily true. There's a Disneyland in Paris, Tokyo, Hong Kong, and Shanghai

Converse: If I am in California, then I am at Disneyland. (False: You can be in California without being at Disneyland).

Inverse: If I am not at Disneyland, then I am not in California. (False: You can be elsewhere in California).

Contrapositive: If I am not in California, then I am not at Disneyland. (False: If I am in Tokyo or Paris, I can be in Disneyland).

39) This statement is true.

Converse: If two lines intersect at exactly one point, then they intersect. (True).

Inverse: If two lines do not intersect, then they do not intersect at exactly one point. (True).

Contrapositive: If two lines do not intersect at exactly one point, then they do not intersect. (True).

40) This statement is true.

Converse: If the angles opposite two sides of a triangle are congruent, then the two sides are congruent. (True).

Inverse: If two sides of a triangle are not congruent, then the angles opposite those sides are not congruent. (True).

Contrapositive: If the angles opposite two sides of a triangle are not congruent, then the two sides are not congruent. (True).

41) True.

Conditional Statement 1: If a whole number is prime, then it has exactly two distinct factors.

Conditional Statement 2: If a whole number has exactly two distinct factors, then it is prime.

42) True.

Conditional Statement 1: If points are collinear, then there is a line that contains the points.

Conditional Statement 2: If there is a line that contains the points, then the points are collinear.

43) True.

Conditional Statement 1: If $5x = 15$, then $x = 3$.

Conditional Statement 2: If $x = 3$, then $5x = 15$.

44) Biconditional: A shape is a rectangle if and only if it has four right angles.

45) Conditional Statement 1: If a polygon is regular, then all its sides and angles are congruent.

Conditional Statement 2: If all the sides and angles of a polygon are congruent, then the polygon is regular.

46) Biconditional: A number is odd if and only if it cannot be divided evenly by 2.

47) AD = AB + BC + CD and FC = FE + ED + DC

AB + BC = FE + ED → AD = FC

48) True

50) False

49) True

51) True

52)

****	6	12	16	32
Sarah		✓		
Jack	✓			
Jacob			✓	
David				✓

53) $a + b$

55) $c + 3$

54) 6

56) $8a + 12$

Effortless

Math

Education

57) Using the Segment Addition Postulate: if O, P, and Q are collinear, then $OP + PQ = OQ$. $7 + 7 = 14$, which is not equal to 12. Therefore, the three points are not collinear. Since $OQ \neq OP + PQ$, P is not the midpoint of segment OQ.

58) To find $m\angle UVW$, subtract $m\angle RST$ from 180°: $180° - 60° = 120°$. Since $m\angle UVW = 120°$ and it is greater than 90°, $\angle UVW$ is an obtuse angle.

59) This is using the Substitution Property of Equality.

60) If two triangles have all three pairs of corresponding sides congruent, then the triangles are congruent by the Side-Side-Side (SSS) Postulate.

61) The Symmetric Property of Equality states that if $a = b$, then $b = a$. Using this property, we can deduce that if $x = 5$ and $5 = y$, then $x = y$.

62) Line AB and line AC from the triangle ABC are intersecting. A is on both lines. B is only on the line AB and C is only on line AC. Because B and C are not on the same line, A, B and C are noncollinear. We know three noncollinear points make a plane. So, A, B and C determine a plane.

63) We know that $\overline{BD} = \overline{DC}$ (definition of midpoint) and we know that triangle LDB is isosceles, because $\angle L \cong \angle B$. In an isosceles triangle both legs are equal. Therefore $\overline{LD} = \overline{DB}$ and $\overline{LD} = \overline{DC}$ and finally $\overline{LD} \cong \overline{DC}$.

64) We know that $\overline{AB} = \overline{BC}$ and $\overline{CD} = \overline{DE}$ (definition of midpoint) and $\overline{AB} = \overline{DE}$ (given). By using the segment addition postulate we have: $AC = AB + BC$, $CE = CD + DE$ and $AE = AC + CE$. By substitution we have:

$AE = AB + BC + CD + DE$ and $AE = AB + AB + AB + AB$ (substitution).

Finally, by simplifying: $AE = 4AB$

65)

Statement	Reason
1) A, B, C, D and E are collinear, in that order.	1) Given
2) $AB = DE$	2) Given
3) $BD = BD$	3) Reflexive *PoE*
4) $AB + BD = DE + BD$	4) Addition *PoE*
5) $AB + BD = AD$ $DE + BD = BE$	5) Segment Addition Postulate
6) $AD = BE$	6) Substitution or Transitive *PoE*

66)

Statement	Reason
1) $\alpha \cong \angle\beta$	1) Given
2) $u \perp v$	2) Given
3) $\angle\theta \cong \angle\lambda$	3) Given
4) $\angle\alpha = \angle\beta$	4) $\cong$ angles have = measures
5) $\angle\lambda \cong \angle\gamma + \angle\delta$	5) Vertical Angles Theorem
6) $\angle\lambda = \angle\gamma + \angle\delta$	6) $\cong$ angles have = measures
7) $\angle\theta = \angle\lambda$	7) $\cong$ angles have = measures
8) $\angle\theta = \angle\gamma + \angle\delta$	8) Transitive

67)

Statement	Reason
1) $\angle a$ and $\angle b$ are right angles	1) Given
2) $m\angle c = 40°$	2) Given
3) $m\angle a = 90°$ and $m\angle b = 90°$	3) Definition of a right angle
4) $m\angle d = 140°$	4) Definition of supplementary angles
5) $90° + 140° + 40° = 270°$	5) Addition of real numbers
6) $m\angle a + m\angle d + m\angle c = 270°$	6) Substitution

Effortless
Math
Education

68)

Statement	Reason
1) $m\angle BOD = 90°$	1) given
2) $m\angle COD = 35°$	2) given
3) $m\angle AOB = 40°$	3) given
4) $m\angle BOD = m\angle BOC + m\angle COD = 90°$	4) Definition of complementary angles
5) $m\angle BOC + 35° = 90°$	5) Substitution
6) $m\angle BOC = 55°$	6) Subtraction PoE
7) $\angle AOB \cong \angle FOE$	7) Vertical Angles Theorem
8) $m\angle AOB = m\angle FOE$	8) $\cong$ angles have $=$ measures
9) $40° + 55° = 105°$	9) Addition of real numbers
10) $m\angle FOE + m\angle BOC = 105°$	10) Substitution

CHAPTER

3 Coordinate Geometry

Math topics that you'll learn in this chapter:

- ☑ Finding Slope
- ☑ Writing Linear Equations
- ☑ Finding Midpoint
- ☑ Finding Distance of Two Points
- ☑ Finding a Graph's Slope
- ☑ Graphing Lines Using Slope–Intercept Form
- ☑ Writing Linear Equations from Graphs
- ☑ Converting Between Standard and Slope-Intercept Forms
- ☑ Slope-intercept Form and Point-slope Form
- ☑ Write a Point-slope Form Equation from a Graph
- ☑ Writing Linear Equations From Y-Intercept and A Slope
- ☑ Comparison of Linear Functions: Equations and Graphs
- ☑ Equations of Horizontal and Vertical lines
- ☑ Graph a Horizontal or Vertical line
- ☑ Equation of Parallel and Perpendicular Lines

61

Finding Slope

- The slope of a line represents the direction of a line on the coordinate plane.

- A coordinate plane contains two perpendicular number lines. The horizontal line is x and the vertical line is y. The point at which the two axes intersect is called the origin. An ordered pair (x, y) shows the location of a point.

- A line on a coordinate plane can be drawn by connecting two points.

- To find the slope of a line, we need the equation of the line or two points on the line.

- The slope of a line with two points $A(x_1, y_1)$ and $B(x_2, y_2)$ can be found by using this formula: $\frac{y_2 - y_1}{x_2 - x_1} = \frac{rise}{run}$

- The equation of a line is typically written as $y = mx + b$ where m is the slope and b is the y-intercept.

Examples:

Example 1. Find the slope of the line through these two points:

$A(1, -6)\ and\ B(3, 2).$

Solution: Slope $= \frac{y_2 - y_1}{x_2 - x_1}$. Let (x_1, y_1) be $A(1, -6)$ and (x_2, y_2) be $B(3, 2)$.

(Remember, you can choose any point for (x_1, y_1) and (x_2, y_2)).

Then: slope $= \frac{y_2 - y_1}{x_2 - x_1} = \frac{2 - (-6)}{3 - 1} = \frac{8}{2} = 4$

The slope of the line through these two points is 4.

Example 2. Find the slope of the line with equation $y = -2x + 8$

Solution: When the equation of a line is written in the form of $y = mx + b$, the slope is m. In this line: $y = -2x + 8$, the slope is -2.

Writing Linear Equations

- The equation of a line in slope-intercept form: $y = mx + b$

- To write the equation of a line, first identify the slope.

- Find the y-intercept. This can be done by substituting the slope and the coordinates of a point (x, y) on the line.

Examples:

Example 1. What is the equation of the line that passes through $(3, -4)$ and has a slope of 6?

Solution: The general slope-intercept form of the equation of a line is $y = mx + b$, where m is the slope and b is the y-intercept.
By substitution of the given point and given slope:
$y = mx + b \rightarrow -4 = (6)(3) + b$. So, $b = -4 - 18 = -22$, and the required equation of the line is: $y = 6x - 22$

Example 2. Write the equation of the line through two points $A(3, 1)$ and $B(-2, 6)$.

Solution: First, find the slope: $Slop = \frac{y_2 - y_1}{x_2 - x_1} = \frac{6 - 1}{-2 - 3} = \frac{5}{-5} = -1 \rightarrow m = -1$

To find the value of b, use either point and plug in the values of x and y in the equation. The answer will be the same: $y = -x + b$. Let's check both points.
Then: $(3, 1) \rightarrow y = mx + b \rightarrow 1 = -1(3) + b \rightarrow b = 4$
$(-2, 6) \rightarrow y = mx + b \rightarrow 6 = -1(-2) + b \rightarrow b = 4$.
The y-intercept of the line is 4. The equation of the line is: $y = -x + 4$

Example 3. What is the equation of the line that passes through $(4, -1)$ and has a slope of 4?

Solution: The general slope-intercept form of the equation of a line is $y = mx + b$, where m is the slope and b is the y-intercept. By substitution of the given point and given slope: $y = mx + b \rightarrow -1 = (4)(4) + b$
So, $b = -1 - 16 = -17$, and the equation of the line is: $y = 4x - 17$.

Finding Midpoint

- The middle of a line segment is its midpoint.

- The Midpoint of two endpoints $A(x_1, y_1)$ and $B(x_2, y_2)$ can be found using this formula: $M(\frac{x_1+x_2}{2}, \frac{y_1+y_2}{2})$

Examples:

Example 1. Find the midpoint of the line segment with the given endpoints.
$(2, -4), (6, 8)$

Solution: Midpoint $= \left(\frac{x_1+x_2}{2}, \frac{y_1+y_2}{2}\right) \rightarrow (x_1, y_1) = (2, -4)$ and $(x_2, y_2) = (6, 8)$
Midpoint $= \left(\frac{2+6}{2}, \frac{-4+8}{2}\right) \rightarrow \left(\frac{8}{2}, \frac{4}{2}\right) \rightarrow M(4, 2)$

Example 2. Find the midpoint of the line segment with the given endpoints. $(-2, 3), (6, -7)$

Solution: Midpoint $= \left(\frac{x_1+x_2}{2}, \frac{y_1+y_2}{2}\right) \rightarrow (x_1, y_1) = (-2, 3)$ and $(x_2, y_2) = (6, -7)$
Midpoint $= \left(\frac{-2+6}{2}, \frac{3+(-7)}{2}\right) \rightarrow \left(\frac{4}{2}, \frac{-4}{2}\right) \rightarrow M(2, -2)$

Example 3. Find the midpoint of the line segment with the given endpoints. $(7, -4), (1, 8)$

Solution: Midpoint $= \left(\frac{x_1+x_2}{2}, \frac{y_1+y_2}{2}\right) \rightarrow (x_1, y_1) = (7, -4)$ and $(x_2, y_2) = (1, 8)$
Midpoint $= \left(\frac{7+1}{2}, \frac{-4+8}{2}\right) \rightarrow \left(\frac{8}{2}, \frac{4}{2}\right) \rightarrow M(4, 2)$

Example 4. Find the midpoint of the line segment with the given endpoints. $(6, 3), (10, -9)$

Solution: Midpoint $= \left(\frac{x_1+x_2}{2}, \frac{y_1+y_2}{2}\right) \rightarrow (x_1, y_1) = (6, 3)$ and $(x_2, y_2) = (10, -9)$
Midpoint $= \left(\frac{6+10}{2}, \frac{3-9}{2}\right) \rightarrow \left(\frac{16}{2}, \frac{-6}{2}\right) \rightarrow M(8, -3)$

Example 5. Find the midpoint of the line segment with the given endpoints. $(0, -7), (18, -13)$

Solution: Midpoint $= \left(\frac{x_1+x_2}{2}, \frac{y_1+y_2}{2}\right) \rightarrow (x_1, y_1) = (0, -7)$ and $(x_2, y_2) = (18, -13)$
Midpoint $= \left(\frac{0+18}{2}, \frac{-7+(-13)}{2}\right) \rightarrow \left(\frac{18}{2}, \frac{-20}{2}\right) \rightarrow M(9, -10)$

Finding Distance of Two Points

- Use the following formula to find the distance of two points with the coordinates $A(x_1, y_1)$ and $B(x_2, y_2)$:

$$d = \sqrt{(x_2 - x_1)^2 + (y_2 - y_1)^2}$$

Examples:

Example 1. Find the distance between $(4, 2)$ and $(-5, -10)$ on the coordinate plane.

Solution: Use distance of two points formula: $d = \sqrt{(x_2 - x_1)^2 + (y_2 - y_1)^2}$

$(x_1, y_1) = (4, 2)$ and $(x_2, y_2) = (-5, -10)$. Then: $d = \sqrt{(x_2 - x_1)^2 + (y_2 - y_1)^2} \rightarrow$

$$= \sqrt{(-5 - 4)^2 + (-10 - 2)^2} = \sqrt{(-9)^2 + (-12)^2} = \sqrt{81 + 144} = \sqrt{225} = 15$$

Then: $d = 15$

Example 2. Find the distance of two points $(-1, 5)$ and $(-4, 1)$.

Solution: Use distance of two points formula: $d = \sqrt{(x_2 - x_1)^2 + (y_2 - y_1)^2}$

$(x_1, y_1) = (-1, 5)$, and $(x_2, y_2) = (-4, 1)$

Then: $= \sqrt{(x_2 - x_1)^2 + (y_2 - y_1)^2} \rightarrow d = \sqrt{(-4 - (-1))^2 + (1 - 5)^2} =$

$\sqrt{(-3)^2 + (-4)^2} = \sqrt{9 + 16} = \sqrt{25} = 5$. Then: $d = 5$

Example 3. Find the distance between $(-6, 5)$ and $(-1, -7)$.

Solution: Use distance of two points formula: $d = \sqrt{(x_2 - x_1)^2 + (y_2 - y_1)^2}$

$(x_1, y_1) = (-6, 5)$ and $(x_2, y_2) = (-1, -7)$. Then: $d = \sqrt{(x_2 - x_1)^2 + (y_2 - y_1)^2}$

$$d = \sqrt{(-1 - (-6))^2 + (-7 - 5)^2} = \sqrt{(5)^2 + (-12)^2} = \sqrt{25 + 144} = \sqrt{169} = 13$$

Example 4. Find the distance between $(-23, -18)$ and $(-8, -10)$.

Solution: Use distance of two points formula: $d = \sqrt{(x_2 - x_1)^2 + (y_2 - y_1)^2}$

$(x_1, y_1) = (-23, -18)$ and $(x_2, y_2) = (-8, -10)$. Then: $d = \sqrt{(x_2 - x_1)^2 + (y_2 - y_1)^2}$

$$d = \sqrt{(-8 - (-23))^2 + (-10 - (-18))^2} = \sqrt{(15)^2 + (8)^2} = \sqrt{225 + 64}$$

$$= \sqrt{289} = 17$$

Finding a Graph's Slope

- A slope is a ratio that states how high something goes up in contrast to how far it goes across. To find the slope of a line, you need to find two points on the line and calculate both the rise and the run. The rise indicates how high or low you go from Point *A* to Point *B*. The run is how far you go from Point *A* to Point *B*. Once you have those, use this formula, $slope = \frac{rise}{run}$,to get the slope.

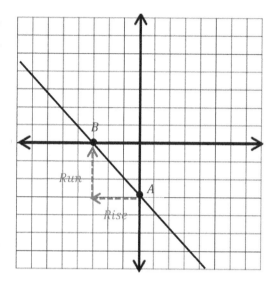

Examples:

Example1. Look at the graph and find the slope of the line.

Solution: To find the slope, select two points on the line, for example $(0, 2)$ and $(3, 3)$. Now use $slope = \frac{rise}{run}$ formula:

$$slope = \frac{rise}{run} = \frac{3 - 2}{3 - 0} = \frac{1}{3}$$

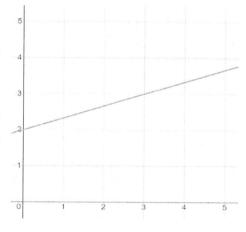

Example2. Look at the graph and find the slope of the line.

Solution: To find the slope, select two points on the line, for example $(0, 1)$ and $(5, 3)$. Now use $slope = \frac{rise}{run}$ formula:

$$slope = \frac{rise}{run} = \frac{3 - 1}{5 - 0} = \frac{2}{5}$$

form:$y = 3x - 6$

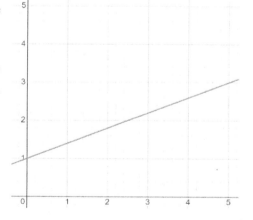

Graphing Lines Using Slope–Intercept Form

- Slope–intercept form of a line: given the slope m and the y-intercept (the intersection of the line and y −axis) b, then the equation of the line is:

$$y = mx + b$$

- To draw the graph of a linear equation in a slope-intercept form on the xy coordinate plane, find two points on the line by plugging two values for x and calculating the values of y.

- You can also use the slope (m) and one point to graph the line.

Example:

Sketch the graph of $y = 2x - 4$.

Solution: To sketch the graph of the equation $y = 2x- 4$, we need to find two points. We can choose two $x -$ values and find their corresponding $y -$ values. Let's choose $x = 0$ and $x = 4$:

When $x = 0: y = 2(0) - 4 \rightarrow y = -4$ So, we have the point $(0, -4)$.

When $x = 4: y = 2(4) - 4 \rightarrow y = 8 - 4 \rightarrow y = 4$ So, we have the point $(4, 4)$.

Now, let's plot these two points and draw a straight line through them:

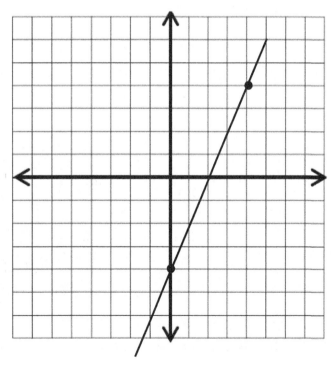

This graph represents the equation $y = 2x - 4$, using the points $(0, -4)$ and $(4, 4)$. The line passes through these points and extends infinitely in both directions.

Writing Linear Equations from Graphs

- How to graph a linear function out:
- A linear equation's slope-intercept form is $y = mx + b$. In this instance, b represents will be the y-intercept, and m is the slope.
- The formula of the slope is $m = \frac{change\ in\ y}{change\ in\ x}$
- To begin, locate the slope, m. Choose a pair of points on the line, then plug them into the formula.
- You can then locate the $y-$intercept. Examine the graph to find the $y-$intercept point, where the line intersects with the $y-$axis.
- Lastly, use the $y-$intercept (b) and the slope (m) to write a slope-intercept equation.

Example:

Look at the graph below. Write the equation of this line in slope-intercept form.

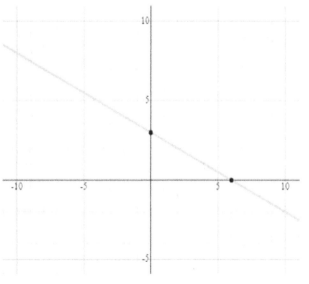

Solution: First, we find the y-intercept of the line according to its intersection with the $y-$ axis. Given that the line intersects the y-axis at point $(0, 3)$, the y-intercept will be equal to $b = 3$. The next step is to find the slope of the line. To find the slope, we need two points, one of which is $(0, 3)$. For the second point, for example, we can choose the intersection point with the x-axis, that is, $(6, 0)$. We use the formula to find the slope:

$$m = \frac{change\ in\ y}{change\ in\ x} = \frac{3 - 0}{0 - 6} = -\frac{1}{2}$$

According to the values of m and b, the formula of the line will be as follows:

$$y = -\frac{1}{2}x + 3$$

Converting Between Standard and Slope-Intercept Forms

- A typical form equation setup is: $Ax + By = C$.

- When set up, a slope-intercept equation form is as follows: $y = mx + b$.

- To move from form to form, change the numbers' order.

- To begin, the Ax should be moved to the equation's opposing side by subtracting or adding it. The equation will look like this: $By = -Ax + C$.

- From there, B should be divided from By, as well as the equation's remainder. This will give you $y = -\frac{Ax}{B} + \frac{C}{B}$.

- With that said, this is no different than the slope-intercept form. Only some letters have been changed.

Examples:

Example 1. Convert the equation of the following line from standard form to Slope-Intercept form. $4x + 12y = 17$

Solution: We subtract $4x$ from both sides of the equation: $12y = -4x + 17$

Then we divide both sides of the equation by the coefficient y, which is 12 in this question:

$$y = -\frac{4}{12}x + \frac{17}{12} \rightarrow y = -\frac{1}{3}x + \frac{17}{12}$$

Example 2. Convert the equation of the following line from standard form to Slope-Intercept form. $13x + 5y = 15$

Solution: We subtract $13x$ from both sides of the equation: $5y = -13x + 15$

Then we divide both sides of the equation by the coefficient y, which is 5 in this question:

$$y = -\frac{13}{5}x + \frac{15}{5} \rightarrow y = -\frac{13}{5}x + 3$$

bit.ly/448gGu6
Find more at

Slope-intercept Form and Point-slope Form

- The point slope form of the equation of a straight line is: $y - y_1 = m(x - x_1)$. The equation is useful when we know: one point on the line: (x_1, y_1) and the slope of the line: m.

- The slope intercept form is probably the most frequently used way to express the equation of a line. In general, the slope intercept form is:

$$y = mx + b$$

Examples:

Example 1. Find the equation of a line with point $(1,5)$ and slope -3, and write it in slope-intercept and point-slope forms.

Solution: For point-slope form, we have the point and slope:

$$x_1 = 1, y_1 = 5, m = -3$$

Then: $y - y_1 = m(x - x_1) \rightarrow y - 5 = -3(x - 1)$

The slope-intercept form of a line is: $y = mx + b$

Since $y = 5, x = 1, m = -3$, we just need to solve for b

$$y = mx + b \rightarrow 5 = -3(1) + b \rightarrow b = 8$$

Slope-intercept form: $y = -3x + 8$

Example 2. Find the equation of a line with point $(4,6)$ and slope 3, and write it in slope-intercept and point-slope forms.

Solution: For point-slope form, we have the point and slope:

$$x_1 = 4, y_1 = 6, m = 3$$

Then: $y - y_1 = m(x - x_1) \rightarrow y - 6 = 3(x - 4)$

The slope-intercept form of a line is: $y = mx + b$

Since $y = 6, x = 4, m = 3$, we just need to solve for b

$$y = mx + b \rightarrow 6 = 3(4) + b \rightarrow b = -6$$

Slope-intercept form: $y = 3x - 6$

Write a Point-slope Form Equation from a Graph

- The usage of the point-slope form equation is to determine the equation of a straight line when passes through a given point. In fact, you can use the point-slope formula only when you have the line's slope and a given point on the line. A line's equation with the slope of $'m'$ that passes through the point (x_1, y_1) can be found by the point-slope formula.

- The point-slope form equation is $y - y_1 = m(x - x_1)$. In this equation, (x, y) is considered as a random point on the line and m is a sign to represent the line's slope.

- To find the point-slope form equation of a straight line and solve it, you can follow the following steps:

  - 1st step: Find the slope, 'm' of the straight line. the slope formula is $m = \frac{change\ in\ y}{change\ in\ x}$. Then find the coordinates (x_1, y_1) of the random point on the line.
  - 2nd step: Put the values you found in the first step in the point-slope formula: $y - y_1 = m(x - x_1)$
  - 3rd step: Simplify the given equation to get the line's equation in the standard form.

Example:

According to the following graph, what is the equation of the line in point-slope form?

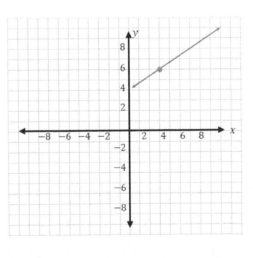

Solution: First, you should find the slope of the line (m). The coordinate of the red point is $(4,6)$. Consider another random point on the line such as $(7,8)$. Put this value in the slope formula: $m = \frac{change\ in\ y}{change\ in\ x} = \frac{8-6}{7-4} = \frac{2}{3} \rightarrow m = \frac{2}{3}$. Now write the equation in point-slope form using the coordinate of the red point is $(4,6)$ and $m = \frac{2}{3}$:

$$y - y_1 = m(x - x_1) \rightarrow y - 6 = \frac{2}{3}(x - 4)$$

Therefore, the equation of the line in point-slope form is:

$$y - 6 = \frac{2}{3}(x - 4)$$

Writing Linear Equations From Y-Intercept and A Slope

- When in slope-intercept form, the equation looks like this: $y = mx + b$ and, as mentioned above (and shown below), "slope" is measured by how much each rise or fall value changes from its predecessor. The intercept of these lines shows you at what point something begins.

- An equation can be written using the y −intercept and slope:

- 1st step: Input the slope m into your slope-intercept formula.

- 2nd step: Input the y-intercept b into your slope-intercept formula. This outcome is the linear equation.

Examples:

Example 1. Write the equation of the line with a y-intercept of -8 and a slope of 6.

Solution: The equation of the line with a y-intercept of -8 and a slope of 6 can be written in slope-intercept form ($y = mx + b$) as $y = 6x - 8$.

Example 2. Write the equation of the line with a y-intercept of 9 and a slope of 1.

Solution: The equation of the line with a y-intercept of 9 and a slope of 1 can be written in slope-intercept form ($y = mx + b$) as $y = x + 9$.

Example 3. Write the equation of the line with a y-intercept of $\frac{3}{4}$ and a slope of 5.

Solution: The equation of the line with a y-intercept of $\frac{3}{4}$ and a slope of 5 can be written in slope-intercept form ($y = mx + b$) as $y = 5x + \frac{3}{4}$.

Example 4. Write the equation of the line with a y-intercept of $\frac{5}{7}$ and a slope of $-\frac{1}{4}$.

Solution: The equation of the line with a y-intercept of $\frac{5}{7}$ and a slope of $-\frac{1}{4}$ can be written in slope-intercept form ($y = mx + b$) as $y = -\frac{1}{4}x + \frac{5}{7}$.

Example 5. Write the equation of the line with a y-intercept of -3 and a slope of -2.

Solution: The equation of the line with a y-intercept of -3 and a slope of -2 can be written in slope-intercept form ($y = mx + b$) as $y = -2x - 3$.

bit.ly/46rGuDb

Find more at

Comparison of Linear Functions: Equations and Graphs

- linear functions are written as follows: $f(x) = mx + b$. In this equation, the y-intercept is represented by b, and the slope is represented by the m.

- A linear function's slope is also referred to as a rate of change. It is calculated as follows: Slope $= \frac{y_2 - y_1}{x_2 - x_1}$. The point where the function intersects with the y-axis is the y-intercept, which has the $(0, b)$ point.

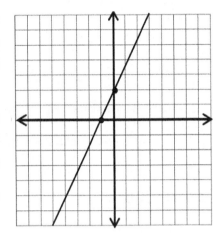

- Graphs, tables, and equations can be used to determine both intercepts and the slope. Such features contrast linear functions against each other.

- Each function's intercepts and rate of change need to be determined to achieve linear function comparisons.

Example:

Which of the following two functions has the greater slope?

Functions A

$$y = \frac{3}{2}x + 1$$

Functions B

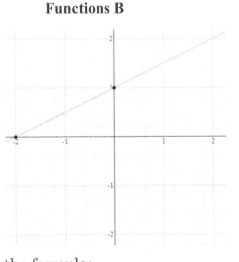

Solution: Considering that the equation of the line is written in slope-intercept form, the slope of the first line becomes $\frac{3}{2}$. To find the slope of the graph function, we need two points, one of which is $(0,1)$. For example, for the second point, we can choose the point of intersection with the x-axis $(-2,0)$. To find the slope, we use the formula:

$$m = \frac{change\ in\ y}{change\ in\ x} = \frac{1 - 0}{0 - (-2)} = \frac{1}{2}$$

So, the slope of function A is greater than function B.

Equations of Horizontal and Vertical lines

- Horizontal lines have a slope of 0. Thus, in the slope-intercept equations $y = mx + b$, $m = 0$, the equation becomes $y = b$, where b is the y-coordinate of the y-intercept.

- Similarly, in the graph of a vertical line, x only takes one value. Thus, the equation for a vertical line is $x = a$, where a is the value that x takes.

Examples:

Example 1. Write an equation for the horizontal line that passes through (6,2).

Solution: Since the line is horizontal, the equation of the line is in the form of:

$$y = b.$$

Where y always takes the same value of 2.

Thus, the equation of the line is:

$$y = 2.$$

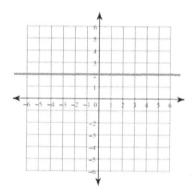

Example 2. Write an equation for the vertical line that passes through (−3,5).

Solution: Since the line is vertical, the equation of the line is in the form of:

$$x = a.$$

Where x always takes the same value of −3.

Thus, the equation of the line is:

$$x = −3.$$

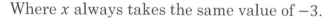

Graph a Horizontal or Vertical Line

- When you graph a line, you usually need a point and the slope of the line to draw the line on the coordinate plane. But there are also exceptions that are called horizontal and vertical lines.

- The horizontal line is a kind of straight line that extends from left to right. An example of a horizontal line can be the x −axis. The horizontal line's slope is always zero because slope can be defined as "rise over run", and a horizontal line's rise is 0. Since the answer of dividing zero by any number is equal to zero, a horizontal line's slope always is zero. Horizontal lines are always parallel to the x −axis and they are written in the form $y = a$ where a is a real number.

- The vertical line is a kind of straight line that extends up and down. An example of a vertical line can be the y −axis. The vertical line's slope is always undefined because the run of a vertical line is zero. In fact, a number's quotient divided by zero is undefined, so a vertical line's slope is always undefined. Vertical lines are always parallel to the y −axis and They are written in the form $x = a$ where a is a real number.

Examples:

Example 1. Graph this equation: $y = -5$

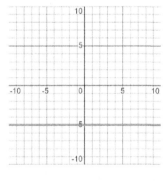

Solution: $y = -5$ is a horizontal line and this equation tells you that every y −value is −5. You can consider some points that have a y −value of −5, then draw a line that connects the points.

Example 1. Graph this equation: $x = 3$

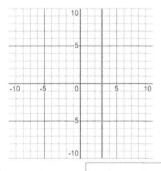

Solution: $x = 3$ is a vertical line and this equation tells you that every x −value is 3. You can consider some points that have an x −value of 3, then draw a line that connects the points.

bit.ly/3D6lORj

Find more at

Equation of Parallel and Perpendicular Lines

- Parallel lines have the same slope.

- Perpendicular lines have opposite-reciprocal slopes. If the slope of a line is m, its Perpendicular line has a slope of $-\frac{1}{m}$.

- Two lines are Perpendicular only if the product of their slopes is negative 1. $m_1 \times m_2 = -1$.

Examples:

Find the equation of a line that is:

Example 1. Parallel to $y = 2x + 1$ and passes though the point $(5,4)$.

Solution: The slope of $y = 2x + 1$ is 2. We can solve it using the "point-slope" equation of a line: $y - y_1 = 2(x - x_1)$ and then put in the point $(5,4)$:
$y - 4 = 2(x - 5)$.
You can also write it in slope intercept format: $y = mx + b$.
$y - 4 = 2x - 10 \rightarrow y = 2x - 6$.

Example 2. Perpendicular to $y = -4x + 10$ and passes though the point $(7,2)$.

Solution: The slope of $y = -4x + 10$ is -4. The negative reciprocal of that slope is: $m = \frac{-1}{-4} = \frac{1}{4}$. So, the perpendicular line has a slope of $\frac{1}{4}$.
Then: $y - y_1 = (\frac{1}{4})(x - x_1)$ and now put in the point $(7,2)$: $y - 2 = (\frac{1}{4})(x - 7)$.
Slope intercept $y = mx + b$ form: $y - 2 = \frac{x}{4} - \frac{7}{4} \rightarrow y = \frac{1}{4}x + \frac{1}{4}$

Example 3. Parallel to $y = 5x - 3$ and passes though the point $(4, -1)$.

Solution: The slope of $y = 5x - 3$ is 5. We can solve it using the "point-slope" equation of a line: $y - y_1 = 5(x - x_1)$ and then put in the point $(4, -1)$: $y - (-1) = 5(x - 4)$.

You can also write it in slope intercept format:
$$y = mx + b. \, y + 1 = 5x - 20 \rightarrow y = 5x - 21$$

Chapter 3: Practices

✎ Find the slope of each line.

1) $y = x - 5$

2) $y = 2x + 6$

3) $y = -5x - 8$

4) Line through $(2, 6)$ and $(5, 0)$

5) Line through $(8, 0)$ and $(-4, 3)$

6) Line through $(-2, -4)$ and $(-4, 8)$

✎ Solve.

7) What is the equation of a line with slope 4 and intercept 16 ? _____

8) What is the equation of a line with slope 3 and passes through point $(1, 5)$? _____

9) What is the equation of a line with slope -5 and passes through point $(-2, 7)$? _____

10) The slope of a line is -4 and it passes through point $(-6, 2)$. What is the equation of the line? _____

11) The slope of a line is -3 and it passes through point $(-3, -6)$. What is the equation of the line? _____

✎ Find the midpoint of the line segment with the given endpoints.

12) $(5, 0), (1, 4)$

13) $(2, 3), (4, 7)$

14) $(8, 1), (2, 5)$

15) $(5, 10), (3, 6)$

16) $(4, -1), (-2, 7)$

17) $(2, -5), (4, 1)$

18) $(7, 6), (-5, 2)$

19) $(-2, 8), (4, -6)$

Effortless Math Education

✎ **Find the distance between each pair of points.**

20) $(-2, 8), (-6, 8)$ 25) $(4, 3), (7, -1)$

21) $(4, -4), (14, 20)$ 26) $(2, 6), (10, -9)$

22) $(-1, 9), (-5, 6)$ 27) $(3, 3), (6, -1)$

23) $(0, 3), (4, 3)$ 28) $(-2, -12), (14, 18)$

24) $(0, -2), (5, 10)$ 29) $(2, -2), (12, 22)$

✎ **Look at the graphs and find the slope of the line.**

30)   31)

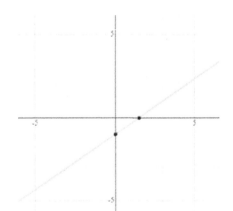   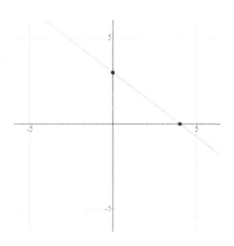

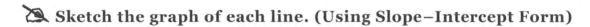 **Sketch the graph of each line. (Using Slope–Intercept Form)**

32) $y = x + 4$ 33) $y = 2x - 5$

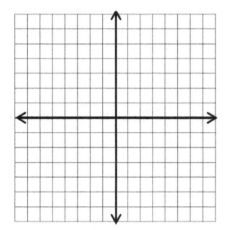   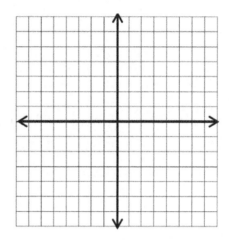

Look at the graph below. Write the equation of this line in slope-intercept form.

34)   35)

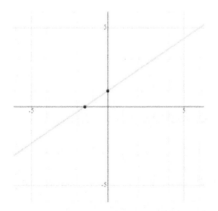   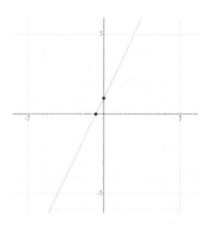

✎ **Convert the equation of the following line from standard form to Slope-Intercept form.**

36) $6x + 13y = 12$

38) $3x - y = -17$

37) $7x + 14y = 21$

39) $-5x + 4y = 20$

✎ **Write the equation of the graphs below in slope-intercept form?**

40)

41)

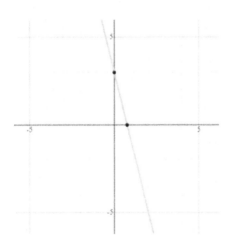

✎ **Find the equation of each line.**

42) Through: $(6, -6)$, slope $= -2$

Point-slope form: _____

Slope-intercept form: _____

43) Through: $(-7, 7)$, slope $= 4$

Point-slope form: _____

Slope-intercept form: _____

Write an equation of each the following line in *point*-slope from.

44) _____

45) _____

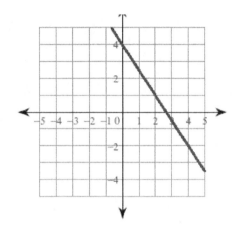

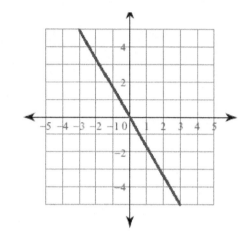

 Solve.

46) Write the equation of the line with a y −intercept of $\frac{9}{11}$ and a slope of $-\frac{1}{7}$.

47) Write the equation of the line with a y −intercept of 0 and a slope of 10.

48) Write the equation of the line with a y −intercept of $-\frac{3}{10}$ and a slope of -4.

49) Write the equation of the line with a y −intercept of 17 and a slope of 1.

50) Write the equation of the line with a y −intercept of -6 and a slope of -1.

51) Write the equation of the line with a y −intercept of $\frac{7}{3}$ and a slope of $-\frac{5}{6}$.

Effortless Math Education

✎ **Compare the slope of the function _A_ and function _B_.**

52) Function _A_:
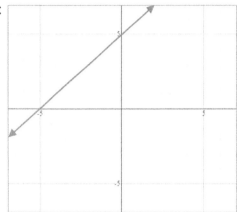
Function _B_: $y = 6x - 3$

53) Function _A_:
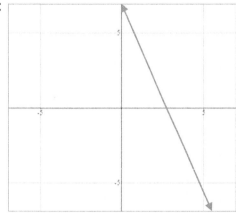
Function _B_: $y = -2.5x - 1$

54) Function _A_:
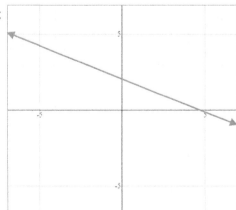
Function _B_: $y = 2x - 1$

✎ **Sketch the graph of each line.**

55) Vertical line that passes through (2,6).

56) Horizontal line that passes through (5,3).

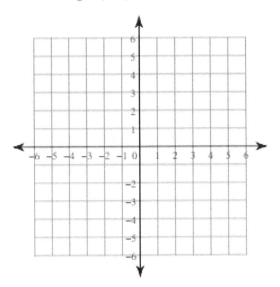

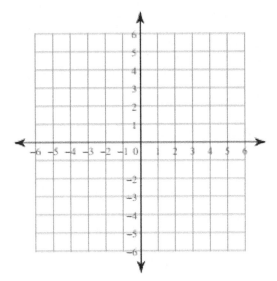

✎ **Find the equation of each line with given information.**

57) Through: $(4, 4)$

Parallel to $y = -6x + 5$

Equation: _____

58) Through: $(7,1)$

Perp. to $y = -\frac{1}{2}x - 4$

Equation: _____

59) Through: $(2,0)$

Parallel to $y = x$

Equation: _____

60) Through: $(0, -4)$

Perp. to $y = 2x + 3$

Equation: _____

61) Through: $(-1,1)$

Parallel to $y = 2$

Equation: _____

62) Through: $(3,4)$

Perp. to $y = -x$

Equation: _____

Effortless
Math
Education

Chapter 3: Answers

1) 1

2) 2

3) −5

4) −2

5) $-\frac{1}{4}$

6) −6

7) $y = 4x + 16$

8) $y = 3x + 2$

9) $y = -5x - 3$

10) $y = -4x - 22$

11) $y = -3x - 15$

12) $(3, 2)$

13) $(3, 5)$

14) $(5, 3)$

15) $(4, 8)$

16) $(1, 3)$

17) $(3, -2)$

18) $(1, 4)$

19) $(1, 1)$

20) 4

21) 26

22) 5

23) 4

24) 13

25) 5

26) 17

27) 5

28) 34

29) 26

30) $\frac{2}{3}$

31) $-\frac{3}{4}$

32) $y = x + 4$

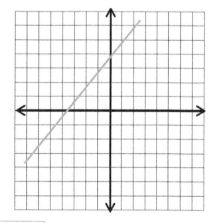

33) $y = 2x - 5$

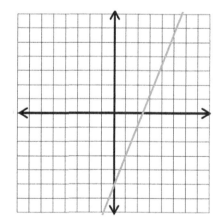

34) $y = \frac{2}{3}x + 1$

35) $y = 2x + 1$

36) $y = -\frac{6}{13}x + \frac{12}{13}$

37) $y = -\frac{1}{2}x + \frac{3}{2}$

38) $y = 3x + 17$

39) $y = \frac{5}{4}x + 5$

40) $y = -4x + 3$

41) $y = 3x - 4$

42) Point-slope form: $y + 6 = -2(x - 6)$

   Slope-intercept form: $y = -2x + 6$

43) Point-slope form: $y - 7 = 4(x + 7)$

   Slope-intercept form: $y = 4x + 35$

44) $y - 1 = -\frac{3}{2}(x - 2)$

45) $y = -\frac{5}{3}x$

46) $y = -\frac{1}{7}x + \frac{9}{11}$

47) $y = 10x$

48) $y = -4x - \frac{3}{10}$

49) $y = x + 17$

50) $y = -x - 6$

51) $y = -\frac{5}{6}x + \frac{7}{3}$

52) The slope of function A is 1 and is lower that than the slope of function B (6).

53) Two functions are parallel.

54) Two functions are perpendicular.

55)

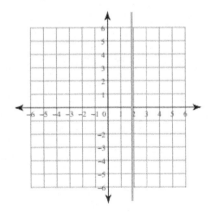

56)

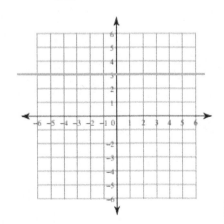

Effortless
Math
Education

57) $y = -6x + 28$

58) $y = 2x - 13$

59) $y = x - 2$

60) $y = -\frac{1}{2}x - 4$

61) $y = 1$

62) $y = x + 1$

4 Transformations, Rigid Motions, and Congruence

Math topics that you'll learn in this chapter:

- ☑ Transformations on the Coordinate Plane
- ☑ Transformations-rotations, reflections and translations
- ☑ Rotation on the Coordinate Plane
- ☑ Reflection on the Coordinate Plane
- ☑ Dilation on the Coordinate Plane
- ☑ Dilations: Finding the Scale Factor
- ☑ Dilations: Finding a Coordinate
- ☑ Translations on the Coordinate Plane
- ☑ Congruence and Rigid Motions
- ☑ Symmetries of a Figure

Translations on the Coordinate Plane

- A translation on the coordinate plane is a type of geometric transformation that moves every point of a figure the same distance in the same direction. This operation slides a figure or a point to a new location without altering its size or shape. Imagine that the figure is on a piece of transparent material, and you're just sliding it around on top of the plane without twisting, flipping, or resizing it.

- For any given point, the move can be defined by a pair of numbers, written as (a, b). Here, $'a'$ represents the horizontal shift (left or right along the x−axis), and $'b'$ represents the vertical shift (up or down along the y−axis). These shifts are also often referred to as the components of a translation vector.

- The general rule for a translation is expressed by the coordinate notation: $(x, y) \rightarrow (x + a, y + b)$. This means that if you have a point (x, y) and you translate it by (a, b), you end up with a new point: $(x + a, y + b)$.

Example:

Translate triangle BGT +5 units in the x−direction and +3 units in the y−direction.

Solution: First, write the original coordinates of the points:

$B = (-3, -5)$ $G = (-3, -1)$ $T = (-1, -1)$

Use this coordinate notation for translating each point: $(x, y) \rightarrow (x + a, y + b)$

$a = +5, b = +3,$ then: $(x, y) \rightarrow (x + 5, y + 3)$

Then: $B' = (2, -2), G' = (2, 2), T' = (4, 2)$

Now, find new points on the coordinate plane and graph the new triangle by B', G', T' coordinates.

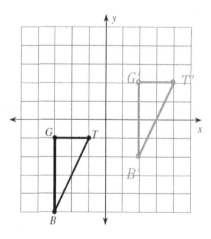

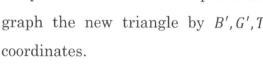

Transformations-rotations, reflections and translations

- Transformation refers to the movement of objects in the coordinate plane.

- Three types of transformation in the coordinately plane:

- Reflection, Rotation and Translation.

- Reflection is flipping an object across a line without changing its size or shape.

- Rotation is rotating an object about a fixed point without changing its size or shape.

- Translation is sliding a figure in any direction without its size, shape or orientation.

Examples:

Determine whether the given picture represents a reflection, rotation or translation.

Example 1.

Solution: The figure has been flipped over the line. So, the given picture represents a reflection.

Example 2.

Solution: The figure has been rotated. So, the given picture represents a rotation.

Rotations on the Coordinate Plane

- In the field of geometry, a rotation is a specific type of transformation where an object is spun around a fixed point, often referred to as the center of rotation. This process can occur in two directions: clockwise or counterclockwise.

- When it comes to rotating objects on a coordinate plane, we often refer to the center of this plane, the origin, as our center of rotation. Three common angles of rotation are 90 degrees, 180 degrees, and 270 degrees, all in a counterclockwise direction.

- When we say, "rotate a shape 90 degrees counterclockwise," it means that each point in the shape moves to a new location according to the rule $(x, y) \rightarrow (-y, x)$.

- "Rotate a shape 180 degrees" refers to spinning the shape half a full turn around the origin. The rule for this rotation is $(x, y) \rightarrow (-x, -y)$.

- Lastly, to "rotate a shape 270 degrees counterclockwise," means to move each point in the shape almost full circle around the origin. The rule for this rotation is $(x, y) \rightarrow (y, -x)$.

Example:

Triangle ABC has vertices $A = (4, 5), B = (5, 1), C = (1, 1)$. Graph triangle ABC and its image after a rotation of $90°$ about the origin.

Solution: The rule for rotating a shape 90 degrees is: $(x, y) \rightarrow (-y, x)$

$$A = (4, 5) \rightarrow A' = (-5, 4)$$

$$B = (5, 1) \rightarrow B' = (-1, 5)$$

$$C = (1, 1) \rightarrow C' = (-1, 1)$$

Graph ΔABC and its image $\Delta A'B'C'$.

Reflections on the Coordinate Plane

- Reflection is flipping an object across a line without changing its size or shape.

- The reflection of the point (x, y) across the x −axis is the point $(x, -y)$.

- The reflection of the point (x, y) across the y −axis is the point $(-x, y)$.

- The reflection of the point (x, y) across the line $y = x$ is the point (y, x).

- The reflection of the point (x, y) across the line $y = -x$ is the point $(-y, -x)$.

- When reflecting a point in the origin, both the x-coordinate and the y-coordinate are negated. $(x, y) \rightarrow (-x, -y)$

Example:

Graph the image of the figure using the transformation given.

Reflection across the x −axis.

Solution: Find the original coordinates:

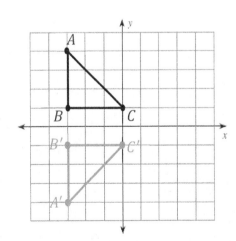

$A = (-3, 4)$

$B = (-3, 1)$

$C = (0, 1)$

The reflection of the point (x, y) across the x −axis is the point $(x, -y)$, So:

$A' = (-3, -4)$

$B' = (-3, -1)$

$C' = (0, -1)$

The image of triangle ABC is $A'B'C'$. (The mark (') is called prime.)

bit.ly/3DLb6VBh

Find more at

Dilation on the Coordinate Plane

- A dilation is a type of transformation that creates an image that is the same shape as the original but in a different size.

- In a Dilation, each point of an object is moved along a straight line. The straight line is drawn from a fixed point called the center of dilation. The distance the points move depends on the scale factor. The center of dilation is the only invariant point.

- Scale factor: $\frac{image\ length}{original\ length} = \frac{distance\ of\ image\ from\ center\ of\ dilation}{distance\ of\ object\ from\ center\ of\ dilation}$

- If the scale factor is greater than 1, the image is an enlargement.

- If the scale factor is between 0 and 1, the image is a reduction.

Example:

Dilate the image of rectangle $ABCD$ by a scale factor of 2 with the origin as the center of dilation.

Solution: First, find the original coordinates:

$$A = (-2, 1), B = (2, 1), C = (-2, -1), D = (2, -1)$$

Next, take all of the coordinates, and multiply them by 2:

$$A' = (-4, 2), B' = (4, 2), C' = (-4, -2), D' = (4, -2)$$

Now, graph the new image.

Since the new figure is larger and our scale factor is greater than 1, the new image is an enlargement.

Dilations: Finding the Scale Factor

- To dilate a figure, you need to define the scale factor. This is accomplished by taking the pre-image size and finding the equivalent side in the post-image. The scale factor refers to the amount by which the pre-image must be multiplied in order to match the post-image. After you have identified your scale factor, you will be able to choose a series of points in the image, as well as the pre-image. The number (x_1, y_1) can be a pre-image point. The other point, (x_2, y_2), is a point in the dilation image. To determine coordinates for the dilation's center $(x_o, $ and $y_o)$, solve the two equations below:

$$\left(xo = \frac{kx_1 - x_2}{k - 1}, yo = \frac{ky_1 - y_2}{k - 1}\right)$$

Examples:

Example 1. In a dilation, triangle ABC becomes triangle $A'B'C'$. What is the scale factor of the dilation?

Solution: To calculate the scale factor of the dilation, calculate the ratio of the length of one side of triangle $A'B'C'$ to the ratio of the length of the corresponding side in triangle ABC. For example, use sides $A'B'$ and AB:

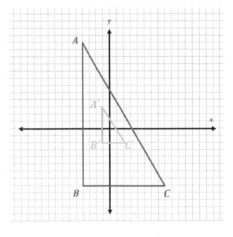

The scale factor $= \frac{5}{20} = \frac{1}{4}$

Example 2. In a dilation, rectangle $ABCD$ becomes rectangle $A'B'C'D'$. What is the scale factor of the dilation?

Solution: To calculate the scale factor of the dilation, calculate the ratio of the length of one side of rectangle $A'B'C'D'$ to the ratio of the length of the length corresponding side in rectangle $ABCD$. For example, use sides $A'B'$ and AB:

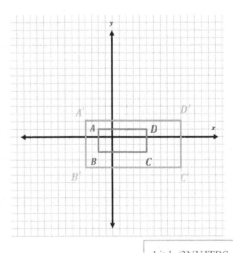

The scale factor $= \frac{6}{3} = 2$

Dilations: Finding a Coordinate

- Dilation can be described as a change in the dimensions and position of a point or figure. The center point of dilation (a reference point) determines the appropriate scale of a figure's dilation. Given a particular a point on a pre-image, (x_1, y_1), along with a corresponding point found on the dilated image, (x_2, y_2), as well as the scale factor, k, the dilation center's location, (x_o, y_o) is $(x_o = \frac{kx_1 - x_2}{k-1}, y_o = \frac{ky_1 - y_2}{k-1})$. The scale factor for dilation will be the proportion of the image's length in relation to the original image's corresponding length. This indicates how much the image expands or shrinks. Dilations have a central point and a scale factor. This is the reference point for dilations, and the scale factor informs how much the figure expands or shrinks. Consequently, given a dilation with known information (such as a central point and scale factor $k > 0$), one can find the new coordinates for any points that were on the original figure.

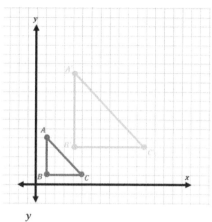

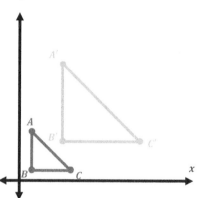

Example:

Get the coordinates of the vertices of the triangle after dilation with a scale factor of 2. The center of dilation is the origin.

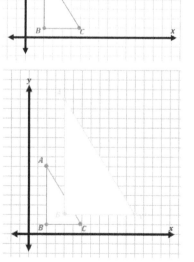

Solution: To find the coordinates of the triangle after dilation, you must multiply the x and y vertices of the initial triangle by the scale factor:

$$A\,(2, 7) \rightarrow A'\,(4, 14)$$
$$B\,(2, 1) \rightarrow B'\,(4, 2)$$
$$C\,(6, 1) \rightarrow C'\,(12, 2)$$

Translations on the Coordinate Plane

- **Properties of Translations:**

  - Preservation of Length and Angle Measures: The distances between points or the angles within a shape are not modified by translations.

  - Parallel Movement: All points in a shape move uniformly in the same direction and distance during a translation.

  - Orientation Preservation: The shape's orientation remains intact after a translation.

- **Describing Translations:** A translation is typically described using a vector that indicates the direction and magnitude of the movement. This vector is denoted as (x, y), where x represents the horizontal shift (right if positive, left if negative) and y is the vertical shift (up if positive, down if negative).

- **Describing Translations:** For a given point $P(a, b)$ and a translation vector (x, y), the new position P' post-translation is: $P'(a + x, b + y)$

Examples:

Example 1. Translate the line segment with two points $A(-1, 1)$ and $B(2, -3)$ on the coordinates, using the translation vector $(-1, 3)$.

Solution: First, draw the line on the coordinates. Then, applying the translation formula for each point of line AB, we get:

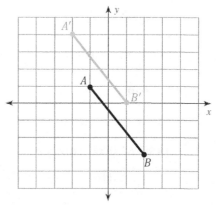

$A'(-1 - 1, 1 + 3) \rightarrow A'(-2, 4)$

$B'(2 - 1, -3 + 3) \rightarrow B'(1, 0)$

Hence, after the translation, point A' is positioned at $(-2, 4)$ and point B' is positioned at $(1, 0)$.
Now, draw the line $A'B'$. On the coordinates.

Example 2. Translate the point $A(3, 4)$ using the translation vector $(2, -3)$.

Solution: Applying the translation formula, we get:
$$A'(3 + 2, 4 - 3) \rightarrow A'(5, 1)$$
Hence, after the translation, point A' is positioned at $(5, 1)$.

bit.ly/49uBmj8

Find more at

Congruence and Rigid Motions

- In geometry, two shapes are congruent if they have the same size and shape. This means that one shape can be transformed into the other through a series of rigid motions without changing its size or shape.

  - Translation: Every point of a shape moves a certain distance in a specific direction.

  - Rotation: The shape is turned around a fixed point called the center of rotation.

  - Reflection: The shape is flipped over a line, producing a mirror image.

  - Glide Reflection: A combination of translation and reflection.

Connection Between Congruence and Rigid Motions: If a shape can be transformed into another solely using rigid motions, then the two shapes are congruent. This offers a dynamic way to understand and prove congruence. Instead of just comparing lengths and angles, one can visualize or demonstrate how one shape can be transformed into another through sequences of translations, rotations, and/or reflections.

Example:

Are triangles *ABC* and *DEF* congruent on the coordinate plane?

Solution: If triangle *ABC* is moved 2 grids down (translated), turned 90° clockwise (rotated), and flipped about the *y* − axis (reflected), it exactly matches with triangle *DEF*.

Therefore, *ABC* is congruent to *DEF*.

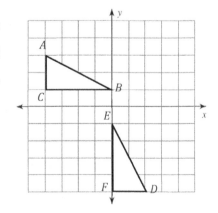

Symmetries of a Figure

- Symmetry in geometry refers to a property where a figure or shape looks the same even after a particular transformation. The most common types of symmetries are:

  ▪ **Reflectional Symmetry (Line Symmetry):** A figure has reflectional symmetry if there's a line over which the figure can be folded so that the two halves match exactly. This line is known as the "axis of symmetry" or "mirror line."

  ▪ **Rotational Symmetry:** A figure possesses rotational symmetry if it can be turned or rotated about a central point and still appear the same as it was before the turn. The smallest angle of rotation that maps the figure onto itself is called the "angle of rotational symmetry."

Examples:

Example 1. where is the symmetry of the figure? and what kind of symmetry is it?

Solution: An isosceles triangle has an axis of symmetry along its altitude from the vertex angle. When folded along this line, the two congruent sides lie on top of one another. The reflection symmetry.

Example 2. What kind of symmetry does the figure have?

Solution: A square has rotational and reflectional symmetry. It can be turned 90°, 180°, 270°, or 360° around its center, and it will still look the same after each turn. Thus, a square has an angle of rotational symmetry of 90°. And it has four axis of symmetry. When folded along these line, the congruent sides lie on top of one another.

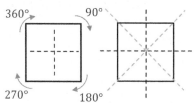

bit.ly/479XjSk

Find more at

Chapter 4: Practices

Determine whether the given picture represents a reflection, rotation and translations.

1)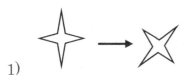

3)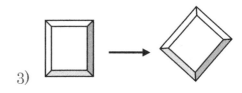

2)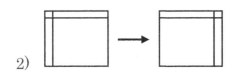

4)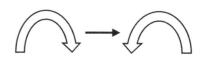

Evaluate.

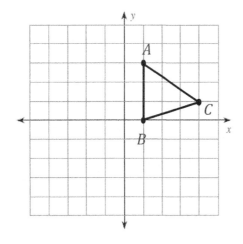

5) Translation: 4 units left and 1 unit down

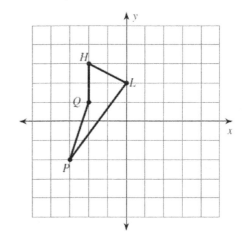

6) Reflection across line: $y = x$

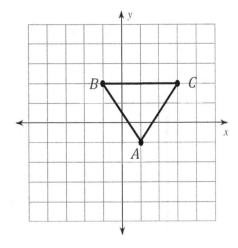

7) Rotation: $90°$

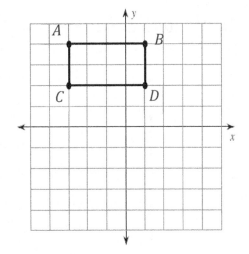

9) Reflection across line: $y = -x$

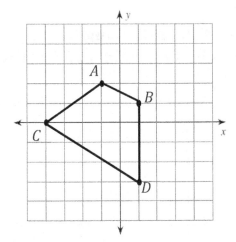

8) Dilation of 0.5.

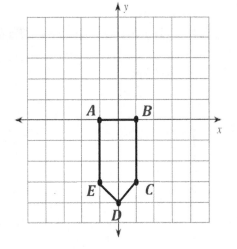

10) Rotation: $270°$

Effortless
Math
Education

✎ **What is the dilation scale factor in the following figures?**

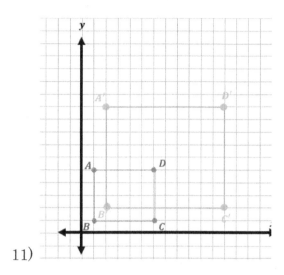

11)

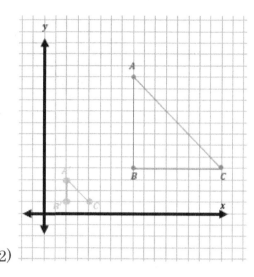

12)

✎ **Get the coordinates of the vertices of the following figures after dilation. The center of dilation is the origin and _k_ is the scale factor.**

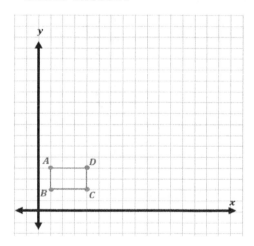

13) k = 3

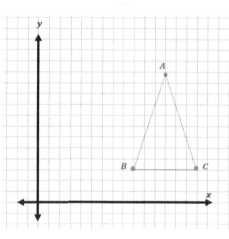

14) k = $\frac{1}{3}$

✍ **Graph the image of the figure using the transformation given.**

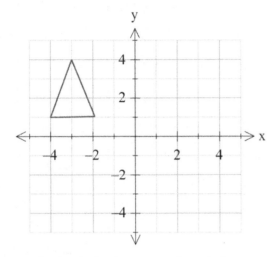

15) Translation: 4 units right

    and 1 unit down

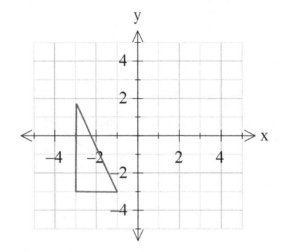

16) Translation: 4 units right

    and 2 unit up

✍ **Write a rule to describe each transformation.**

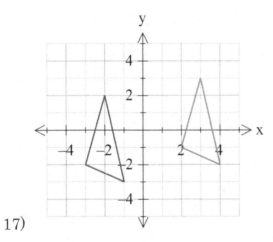

17)

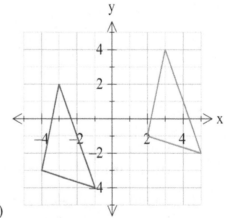

18)

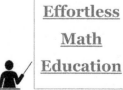

Effortless

Math

Education

✎ **Are the figures congruent on the coordinate planes?**

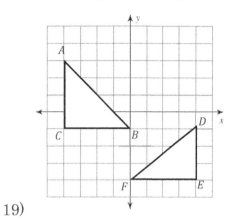

19)

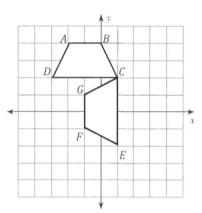

20)

21)

22)

✎ **Solve.**

23) Given an isosceles triangle *ABC* with base *BC* and vertex *A*, if you draw the altitude *AD* from *A* to *BC*, is *AD* the axis of symmetry?

24) Given a parallelogram *ABCD*, if you draw the altitude *HL* from *AB* to *CD*, is *HL* the axis of symmetry?

25) Does the circle have reflection symmetry?

26) how many reflections symmetrical does a regular hexagon have? and how many rotation symmetrical does it have?

Chapter 4: Answers

1) Rotation

2) Reflection

3) Rotation

4) Reflection

5)

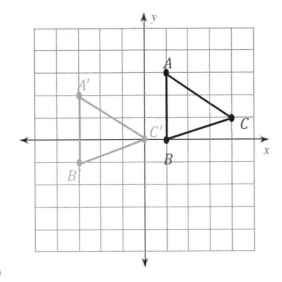

7)

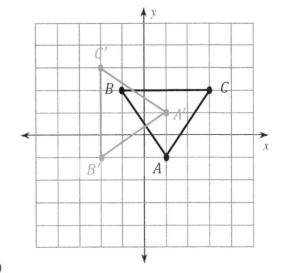

6)

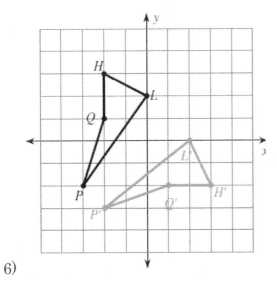

8)

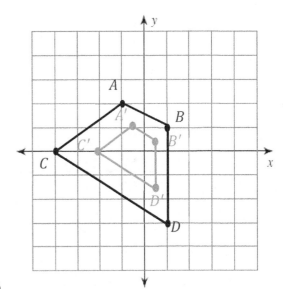

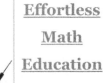

Effortless

Math

Education

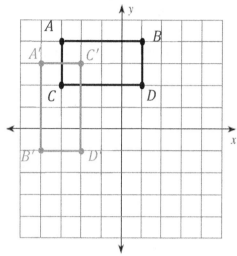

9)

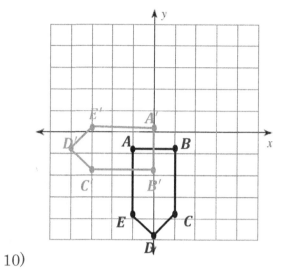

10)

11) 2

12) $\frac{1}{4}$

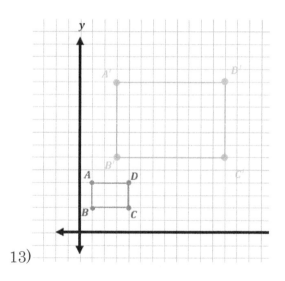

13)

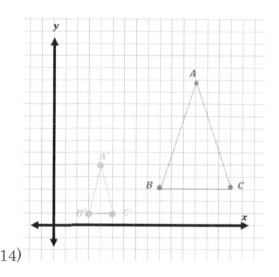

14)

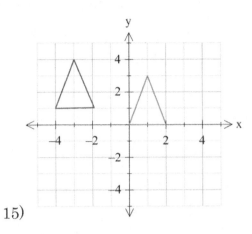

15)

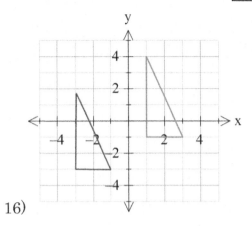

16)

17) Translation: 5 units right and 1 unit up

18) Translation: 6 units right and 2 unit up

19) NO   23) Yes

20) Rotation   24) No,
                              it doesn't have reflection Symmetry.

21) Translation   25) Yes

22) NO   26) 6 and 6

5 Quadrilaterals and Polygons

Math topics that you'll learn in this chapter:

- ☑ Classifying Polygons
- ☑ Angles in Quadrilaterals
- ☑ Properties of Trapezoids
- ☑ Properties of Parallelograms
- ☑ Properties of Rectangles
- ☑ Properties of The Rhombus
- ☑ Properties of Squares
- ☑ Areas of Triangles and Quadrilaterals
- ☑ Perimeter of Polygons
- ☑ Polygons and Angles

107

Classifying Polygons

- Polygons are closed 2 − dimensional shapes made up of straight-line segments. The classification of polygons is based on the number of sides they have and certain other properties.

- By Number of Sides:

  - Triangle: 3 sides
  - Quadrilateral: 4 sides
  - Pentagon: 5 sides
  - Hexagon: 6 sides
  - Heptagon: 7 sides
  - Octagon: 7 sides
  - Nonagon: 9 sides
  - Decagon: 10 sides

  For polygons with more than 10 sides, they are usually referred to by their number: 11 −gon, 12 −gon, and so on.

- By Internal Angles:

  - Convex Polygon: All internal angles are less than 180°.

  - Concave Polygon: At least one internal angle is more than 180°.

- By Length of Sides:

  - Regular Polygon: All sides and angles are equal.

  - Irregular Polygon: Sides and/or angles are not equal.

  - By Symmetry:

  - Symmetrical Polygon: A polygon that can be folded along an axis (or axes) to have its halves match up.

  - Asymmetrical Polygon: A polygon that doesn't have symmetry.

Examples:

Example 1. If a polygon has 8 sides and each internal angle measures 135°, classify the polygon.

Solution: The polygon is an octagon (because it has 8 sides). Since all internal angles are equal, it's a regular polygon. Moreover, as all internal angles are less than 180°, it is convex.

Example 2. What type of polygon is formed if it has 6 sides and not all sides are of equal length?

Solution: The polygon is a hexagon (because it has 6 sides). As not all sides are equal, it's an irregular polygon.

Angles in Quadrilaterals

- The sum of the interior angles of any quadrilateral is 360°.

  - Consider any quadrilateral $ABCD$. Draw a diagonal BD, dividing the quadrilateral into two triangles: ABD and BCD.

  - Since the sum of the angles in any triangle is 180°, the combined angle sum for both triangles is $2 \times 180° = 360°$. Hence, the sum of the angles in the quadrilateral $ABCD$ is also 360°.

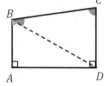

- Types of Quadrilaterals and Their Angles:

  - **Rectangle:** All angles are right angles 90°.

  - **Square:** A special type of rectangle where all angles are 90° and all sides are of equal length.

  - **Rhombus:** All angles are not necessarily 90°, but opposite angles are congruent. And the adjacent angles are supplementary.

  - **Parallelogram:** Opposite angles are congruent, and adjacent angles are supplementary.

  - **Trapezoid:** Only one pair of opposite sides is parallel. The angles don't have a specific relationship, but their sum is still 360°.

Examples:

Example 1. In a parallelogram $ABCD$, if $\angle A$ is 80°, find the measures of $\angle B$, $\angle C$, and $\angle D$.

Solution: Since $ABCD$ is a parallelogram, $\angle A$ is congruent to $\angle C$, and $\angle B$ is congruent to $\angle D$. Thus, $\angle C = 80°$.
$\angle B$ and $\angle D$ are supplementary to $\angle A$ and $\angle C$ respectively, so:
$$\angle B = 180° - 80° = 100°$$
$$\angle D = 180° - 80° = 100°$$

Example 2. In a rhombus $EFGH$, if one angle is 60°, determine the other angles.

Solution: In a rhombus, opposite angles are congruent, and adjacent angles are supplementary. If one angle is 60°, its opposite angle is also 60°. The adjacent angle would be:
$$180° - 60° = 120°$$
So, the angles in the rhombus are 60°, 120°, 60°, and 120°.

Properties of Trapezoids

The following are fundamental properties and characteristics of trapezoids:

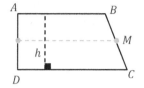

-   **Bases:** The two parallel sides of a trapezoid are called the bases. Let's represent them as AB and CD.

-   **Legs:** The non-parallel sides of a trapezoid are its legs. These can be represented as BC and AD.

-   **Height (or Altitude):** The perpendicular distance between the two bases is the height (h) of the trapezoid.

-   **Base Angles:** The angles that share a common base are called base angles. For instance, angles at base AB are $\angle A$ and $\angle B$, while the angles at base CD are $\angle C$ and $\angle D$.

-   **Isosceles Trapezoid:** If the non-parallel sides (legs) of a trapezoid are congruent, then it's an isosceles trapezoid. An isosceles trapezoid has some additional properties:

    -   The diagonals are congruent.
    -   Both pairs of base angles are supplementary.
    -   The base angles are congruent. ($\angle A \cong \angle B$ and $\angle C \cong \angle D$).

-   **Midsegment (or Median):** This is the segment that joins the midpoints of the non-parallel sides. The length of the midsegment is the average of the lengths of the bases:

$$Midsegment = \frac{(length\ of\ base\ 1 + length\ of\ base\ 2)}{2}$$

Example:

Find the length of the diagonal AC and the length of the median:

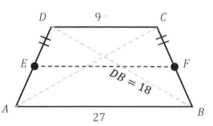

Solution: In an isosceles trapezoid, the diagonals are congruent. So, if DB is equal to 18 then AC is equal to 18, too.

And to find the midsegment, use the formula:

$$m = \frac{\overline{AB} + \overline{DC}}{2} \rightarrow m = \frac{27 + 9}{2} \rightarrow m = \frac{36}{2} \rightarrow m = 18$$

Properties of Parallelograms

If just one pair of opposite sides in a quadrilateral is both parallel and equal, the quadrilateral is a parallelogram. Let's delve into the characteristics and properties of parallelograms:

- **Opposite Sides are Equal:** In parallelogram $ABCD$, $AB \cong CD$ and $BC \cong AD$.

- **Opposite Angles are Equal:** In parallelogram $ABCD$, $\angle A \cong \angle C$ and $\angle B \cong \angle D$.

- **Consecutive Angles are Supplementary:** In parallelogram $ABCD$, $\angle A + \angle B = 180°$ (and similarly for other consecutive angles).

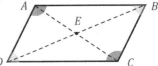

- **Diagonals Bisect Each Other:** In parallelogram $ABCD$, if the diagonals intersect at point E, then $AE \cong CE$ and $BE \cong DE$.

- **Diagonals Create Congruent Triangles:** When you draw the diagonals of a parallelogram, they split the figure into two congruent triangles.

- **Parallelogram Law:** The sum of the squares of the lengths of the diagonals of a parallelogram equals the sum of the squares of the lengths of its sides. If AC and BD are the diagonals and a, b, c, and d are the side lengths, then:

$$AC^2 + BD^2 = a^2 + b^2 + c^2 + d^2$$

Examples:

Example 1. Given parallelogram $ABCD$ with $\overline{AB} = 10$ units and $\angle A = 75°$, determine $\overline{CD}$ and $\angle D$.

Solution: Since opposite sides of a parallelogram are congruent, $\overline{CD} = \overline{AB} = 10$ units. As Consecutive Angles are Supplementary in a parallelogram:

$\angle D + \angle A = 180° \rightarrow \angle D + 75° = 180° \rightarrow \angle D = 105°$.

Example 2. In parallelogram $WXYZ$, if $\overline{WX} = 8$ units and $\overline{WZ} = 10$ units, find $\overline{XY}$ and $\overline{YZ}$.

Solution: Because $\overline{XY}$ is opposite to $\overline{WZ}$, $\overline{XY} = \overline{WZ} = 10$ units. And $\overline{YZ}$ is opposite to $\overline{WX}$, $\overline{YZ} = \overline{WX} = 8$ units.

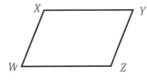

bit.ly/49IMChq

Find more at

Properties of Rectangles

- A rectangle is a special type of parallelogram where all the interior angles are right angles. This characteristic leads to several properties that define a rectangle:

- **All Angles are Right Angles:** Every angle in a rectangle measures 90°.

- **Opposite Sides are Equal:** If $ABCD$ is a rectangle, then $AB \cong CD$ and $BC \cong AD$.

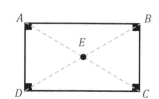

- **Opposite Sides are Parallel:** $AB \parallel CD$ and $BC \parallel AD$.

- **Diagonals are Congruent:** If AC and BD are the diagonals, then $AC \cong BD$.

- **Diagonals Bisect Each Other:** in rectangle $ABCD$, if E is the intersection point of the diagonals, then $AE \cong CE$ and $BE \cong DE$.

- **Diagonals are Perpendicular Bisectors of Each Other:** In a rectangle, the diagonals bisect each other but are not necessarily perpendicular.

Example:

Find the unknown quantities in the following rectangles using it's properties.

If $AC = 16\ cm$, $OD =?$

If $\angle B = 90°$, $\angle C =?$

$AB = 3x - 10$, $DC = 12$, $x =?$

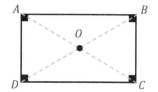

Solution: Since Diagonals Bisect Each Other, $OD = \frac{1}{2}AC = \frac{16}{2} = 8\ cm$.

As All Angles are Right Angles, $\angle C = \angle B = 90°$.

And as Opposite Sides are Equal, $AB = DC \rightarrow 3x - 10 = 16 \rightarrow 3x = 6 \rightarrow x = 2$.

Therefor, $OD = 8\ cm$, $\angle C = 90°$, $x = 2\ cm$.

Properties of The Rhombus

A rhombus is a special type of parallelogram where all four sides are of equal length. This unique feature leads to several defining properties:

- **All Sides are Equal:** If $ABCD$ is a rhombus, then $AB \cong BC \cong CD \cong DA$.

- **Opposite Angles are Equal:** As with all parallelograms, in a rhombus, the opposite angles are congruent. Therefore, in rhombus $ABCD$, $\angle A \cong \angle C$ and $\angle B \cong \angle D$.

- **Opposite Sides are Parallel:** So, in rhombus $ABCD$, $AB \parallel CD$ and $BC \parallel AD$.

- **Diagonals are Perpendicular Bisectors:** In rhombus $ABCD$, diagonal AC is perpendicular to diagonal BD at their point of intersection, E.

- **Diagonals Bisect the Angles:** In a rhombus, each diagonal bisects a pair of opposite angles. For example, in rhombus $ABCD$, diagonal AC bisects angles A and C.

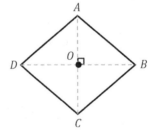

- **Diagonals are Unequal:** While the diagonals of a rectangle are congruent, those of a generic rhombus are not. However, they bisect each other into two congruent segments.

Example:

In rhombus $WXYZ$, if $\overline{WX} = 8$ units and one diagonal $\overline{WY} = 10$ units, and the angle between WY and WX is 60°, find XZ.

Solution: AS diagonals bisect the angles and diagonals are perpendicular bisectors, to find the length of XZ, we can use trigonometry. we have a right-triangles WXO.so:

$$sin60° = \frac{XO}{WX} \rightarrow \frac{\sqrt{3}}{2} = \frac{XO}{8} \rightarrow XO = 4\sqrt{3}$$

Now, we can calculate the length of XZ:

$$XZ = 2XO \rightarrow XZ = 2(4\sqrt{3}) \rightarrow XZ = 8\sqrt{3}$$

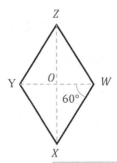

bit.ly/3Sn4QsU

Find more at

Properties of Squares

A square is a quadrilateral that combines the properties of both a rectangle and a rhombus. As such, it is characterized by the following defining properties:

- **All Sides are Equal:** If $ABCD$ is a square, then $AB = BC = CD = DA$.

- **All Angles are Right Angles:** Each interior angle in a square is 90°.

- **Opposite Sides are Parallel:** Thus, in square ABCD, $AB \parallel CD$ and $BC \parallel AD$.

- **Diagonals are Congruent and Perpendicular:** If AC and BD are the diagonals of square $ABCD$, then $AC = BD$ and they intersect at right angles.

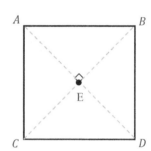

- **Diagonals Bisect the Angles:** In square $ABCD$, diagonal AC bisects angles A and C.

- **Diagonals Bisect Each Other:** The point where the diagonals intersect divides each diagonal into two equal parts. For square $ABCD$ with diagonals intersecting at point E, $AE = CE$ and $BE = DE$.

Example:

In square $PQRS$, if diagonal $PR = 10\sqrt{2}$ units, find the side PQ and the area.

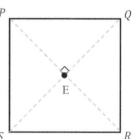

Solution: Using the properties of a $45 - 45 - 90$ right triangle, we have:

$$PQ = \frac{PR}{\sqrt{2}} \rightarrow PQ = \frac{10\sqrt{2}}{\sqrt{2}} \rightarrow PQ = 10$$

Areas of Triangles and Quadrilaterals

Let's explore these areas with their formulas.

- **Triangle:** The area A of a triangle with base b and height h perpendicular to the base is: $A = \frac{1}{2}b \times h$

- **Parallelogram:** The area A of a parallelogram with base b and height h perpendicular to the base is: $A = b \times h$

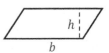

- **Rectangle:** The area A of a rectangle with length l and width w is: $A = l \times w$

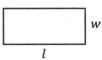

- **Square:** The area A of a square with side s is: $A = s^2$

- **Trapezoid:** The area A of a trapezoid with bases a and b and height h perpendicular to the bases is: $A = \frac{1}{2}(a + b) \times h$

- **Rhombus:** The area A of a rhombus can be determined using its diagonals d_1 and d_2: $A = \frac{1}{2}d_1 \times d_2$

Examples:

Example 1. A parallelogram with a base of 8 units and a height of 5 units has an area of:

Solution: Use the area of the parallelogram formula:
$$A = b \times h = 8 \times 5 = 40 \text{ square units}$$

Example 2. A trapezoid with bases of 6 units and 10 units and a height of 4 units has an area of:

Solution: Use the area of the trapezoid formula:
$$A = \frac{1}{2}(a + b) \times h = \frac{1}{2}(6 + 10) \times 4 = \frac{1}{2} \times 16 \times 4 = 32 \text{ square units}$$

Example 3. A rhombus with diagonals of 8 units and 6 units has an area of:

Solution: Use the area of the rhombus formula:
$$A = \frac{1}{2}d_1 \times d_2 = \frac{1}{2} \times 8 \times 6 = 24 \text{ square units}$$

bit.ly/46UESl6

Find more at

Perimeter of Polygons

-   The perimeter of a square = $4 \times side = 4s$

-   The perimeter of a rectangle = $2(width + length)$

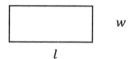

-   The perimeter of trapezoid = $a + b + c + d$

-   The perimeter of a regular hexagon = $6a$

-   The perimeter of a parallelogram = $2(l + w)$

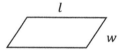

Examples:

Example 1. Find the perimeter of following regular hexagon.

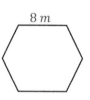

Solution: Since the hexagon is regular, all sides are equal.
Then, the perimeter of the hexagon = $6 \times (one\ side)$
The perimeter of the hexagon = $6 \times (one\ side) = 6 \times 8 = 48\ m$

Example 2. Find the perimeter of following trapezoid.

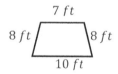

Solution: The perimeter of a trapezoid = $a + b + c + d$
The perimeter of the trapezoid = $7 + 8 + 8 + 10 = 33\ ft$

Example 3. Find the perimeter of following parallelogram.

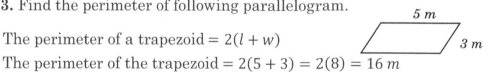

Solution: The perimeter of a trapezoid = $2(l + w)$
The perimeter of the trapezoid = $2(5 + 3) = 2(8) = 16\ m$

Polygons and Angles

- A polygon is a closed figure made up of straight-line segments. The points where the segments meet are called vertices. Let's explore the relationship between polygons and their angles.

- **Interior Angles of a Polygon:** The sum of the interior angles of a polygon can be determined using the formula:
  Sum of interior angles = $(n - 2) \times 180°$
  Where n is the number of sides.

- **Each Interior Angle of a Regular Polygon:** If the polygon is regular (all sides and angles are equal), the measure of each interior angle can be found using:
  Each interior angle = $\frac{(n-2) \times 180°}{n}$

- **Exterior Angles of a Polygon:** The exterior angles are the angles formed outside the polygon when one side is extended. For any polygon, the sum of the exterior angles is always $360°$. For a regular polygon with n sides, each exterior angle is:
  Each exterior angle = $\frac{360°}{n}$

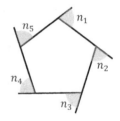

Example:

Find the angles $a°$ and $b°$.

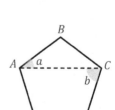

Solution: to find these angles, first calculate the interior angle. Use the formula:

Each interior angle = $\frac{(n-2) \times 180°}{n} = \frac{(5-2) \times 180°}{5} = \frac{540°}{5} = 108°$

It's mean: $a° + b° = 108°$

Now we have an equation by two unknown. Otherwise, we can calculate the angle a by the isosceles triangle, and we know, $\angle A + \angle B + \angle C = 180°$, $\angle B = 108°$, and $\angle A = \angle C$. So:

$\angle A + \angle B + \angle C = 180° \rightarrow \angle A + 108° + \angle A = 180° \rightarrow 2\angle A = 180° - 108° \rightarrow \angle A = 36°$

Then, $a° + b° = 108° \rightarrow 36° + b° = 108° \rightarrow b° = 72°$

Therefore, angle $a°$ is $36°$ and angle $b°$ is $72°$.

bit.ly/49gQvnX

Find more at

Chapter 5: Practices

✎ **State the most specific name for each figure.**

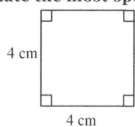

1)

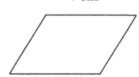

2)

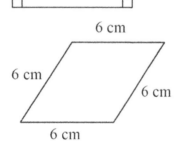

4)

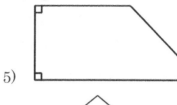

5)

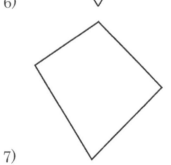

6)

7)

✎ **State all possible name for each figure.**

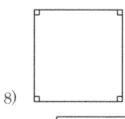

8)

9)

10)

✎ **Find the measure of each angle indicated.**

11)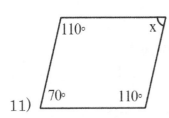

13)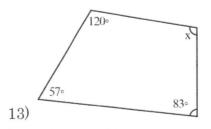

12)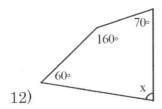

14)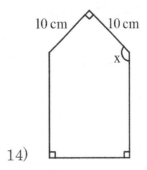

✎ **Solve for x.**

15)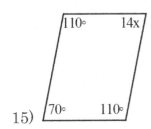

17)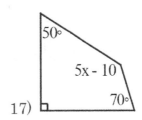

16)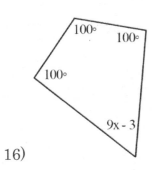

18)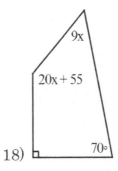

Find the length of the angle indicated for each trapezoid.

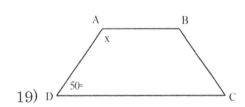

19)

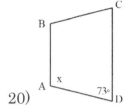

20)

Find the length of the median of each trapezoid.

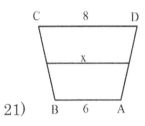

21)

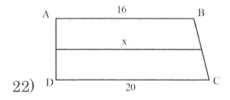

22)

Solve for *x*. Each figure is a trapezoid.

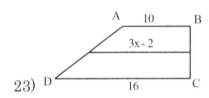

23)

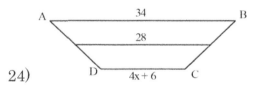

24)

Find the measurement indicated in each parallelogram.

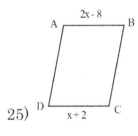

25)

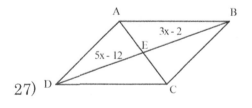

27)

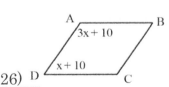

26)

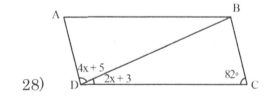

28)

✍ **Solve for x. Each figure is a parallelogram.**

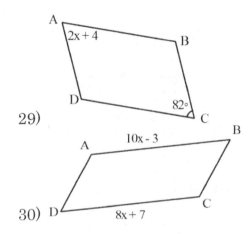

29)

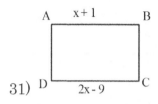

31)

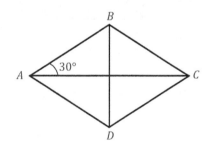

30)

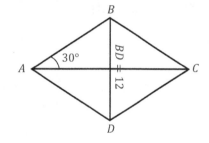

32)

✍ **Find the measurement indicated in each Rhombus. Round your answer to the nearest tenth if necessary.**

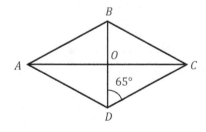

33) $\angle BDC =$ _____

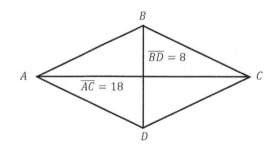

35) $\overline{AD} =$ _____

34) $\angle BAD =$ _____

36) $\angle BAC =$ _____

✏️ **Solve for *x*. Each figure is a Rhombus.**

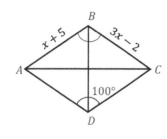

37)

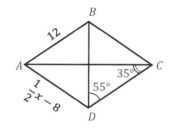

38)

✏️ **Find the measurement indicated in each Squar.**

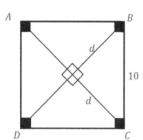

39) $d =$ ____

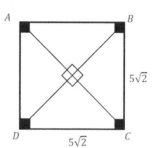

40) $\overline{AC} =$ ____

✏️ **Solve for *x*. Each figure is a Squar.**

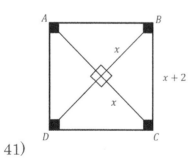

41)

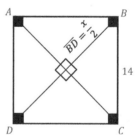

42)

✎ Find the area of each.

43)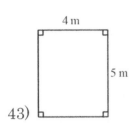

44)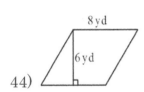

45)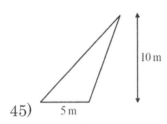

46)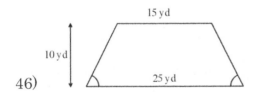

47)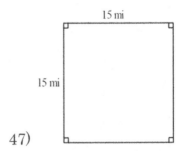

48)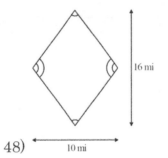

49)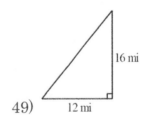

50)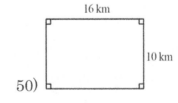

Effortless
Math
Education

✎ **Find the perimeter or circumference of each shape**.

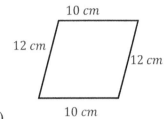

51)

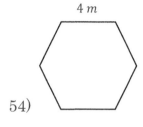

54)

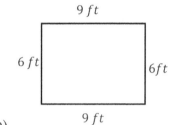

52)

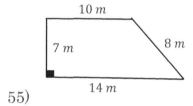

55)

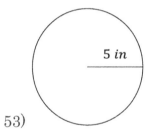

53)

56)

✍ **Find the measure of one interior angle in each polygon. Round your answer to the nearest tenth if necessary.**

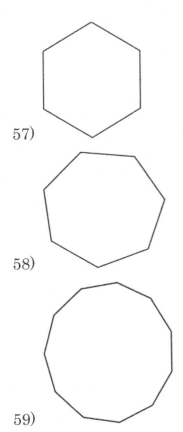

57)

58)

59)

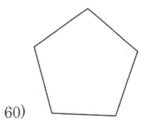

60)

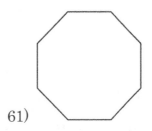

61)

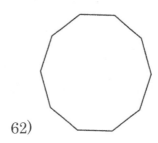

62)

63) Regular 14 −gon

64) Regular quadrilateral

65) Regular 17 −gon

66) Regular 32 −gon

Effortless Math Education

Chapter 5: Answers

1) Square

2) Parallelogram

3) Rectangle

4) Rhombus

5) Trapezoid

6) Kite

7) Quadrilateral

8) quadrilateral, parallelogram, rhombus, rectangle, square

9) quadrilateral, parallelogram, kite, rhombus

10) quadrilateral, trapezoid

11) 70°	20) 107°	30) 5
12) 70°	21) 7	31) 10
13) 100°	22) 18	32) 37
14) 135°	23) 5	33) 60°
15) 5	24) 4	34) 50°
16) 7	25) 12	35) 12
17) 32	26) 130°	36) 24°
18) 5	27) 13	37) 3.5
19) 130°	28) 33°	38) 40
	29) 39	39) $5\sqrt{2}$

40) 10

41) $2(\sqrt{2} + 1)$

42) $28\sqrt{2}$

43) $20\ m^2$

44) $48\ yd^2$

45) $25\ m^2$

46) $200\ yd^2$

47) $225\ mi^2$

48) $50\ mi^2$

49) $96\ mi^2$

50) $160\ km^2$

51) $44\ cm$

52) $30\ ft$

53) $10\ \pi \approx 31.4\ in$

54) $24\ m$

55) $39\ m$

56) $44\ cm$

57) $120°$

58) $128.6°$

59) $147.3°$

60) $108°$

61) $135°$

62) $144°$

63) $154.3°$

64) $90°$

65) $158.8°$

66) $168.7°$

Effortless Math Education

CHAPTER

6 Triangles

Math topics that you'll learn in this chapter:

- ☑ Triangles
- ☑ Classifying Triangles
- ☑ Triangle Angle Sum
- ☑ Triangle Midsegment
- ☑ Angle Bisectors of Triangles
- ☑ Isosceles and Equilateral Triangles
- ☑ Right Triangles
- ☑ Special Right Triangles
- ☑ The Pythagorean Theorem
- ☑ Pythagorean Theorem Converse: Is This a Right Triangle?
- ☑ Geometric Mean in Triangles
- ☑ Exterior Angle Theorem
- ☑ Medians
- ☑ Centroid
- ☑ The Triangle Inequality Theorem
- ☑ SSS and SAS Congruence
- ☑ ASA and AAS Congruence
- ☑ HL Congruences

Triangles

- In any triangle, the sum of all angles is 180 degrees.

- Area of a triangle $= \frac{1}{2}(base \times height)$

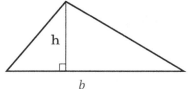

Examples:

Example 1. What is the area of this triangles?

Solution: Use the area formula:

Area $= \frac{1}{2}(base \times height)$

$base = 14$ and $height = 10$, Then:

Area $= \frac{1}{2}(14 \times 10) = \frac{1}{2}(140) = 70$

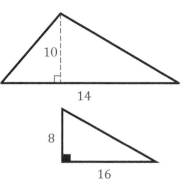

Example 2. What is the area of this triangles?

Solution: Use the area formula:

Area $= \frac{1}{2}(base \times height)$

$base = 16$ and $height = 8$; Area $= \frac{1}{2}(16 \times 8) = \frac{128}{2} = 64$

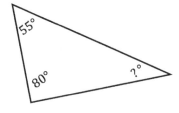

Example 3. What is the missing angle in this triangle?

Solution:

In any triangle, the sum of all angles is 180 degrees.

Let x be the missing angle.

Then: $55 + 80 + x = 180 \rightarrow 135 + x = 180 \rightarrow$

$x = 180 - 135 = 45$

The missing angle is 45 degrees.

Example 4. What is the missing angle in this triangle?

Solution:

In any triangle, the sum of all angles is 180 degrees.

Let x be the missing angle.

Then: $74 + 83 + x = 180 \rightarrow 157 + x = 180 \rightarrow$

$x = 180 - 157 = 23$

The missing angle is 23 degrees.

Classifying Triangles

- Triangles are three-sided polygons, and they can be classified based on their side lengths and internal angles. Here's a breakdown of the classifications:

- Based on Side Lengths:

    - **Equilateral Triangle:** All three sides are of equal length.
    - **Isosceles Triangle:** Two sides are of equal length. The angles opposite the equal sides are also.
    - **Scalene Triangle:** No sides are of equal length. All angles are also different.

- Based on Internal Angles:

    - **Acute Triangle:** All three internal angles are less than 90°.
    - **Right Triangle:** One angle is exactly 90°.
    - **Obtuse Triangle:** One angle is more than 90°.

- **Notes:** A triangle can belong to one classification from each category. For example, a triangle can be both isosceles and acute.

- **Notes:** The sum of the internal angles of any triangle is always 180°.

Examples:

Example 1. If one side of a triangle is 5 units and all its sides are of equal length, what type of triangle is it?

Solution: Equilateral Triangle, because all three sides are of equal length.

Example 2. If the largest angle in a triangle measures 100°, what type of triangle is it based on its angles?

Solution: Obtuse Triangle, because one of the interior angles measures more than 90°. In an obtuse triangle, if one angle measures more than 90°, then the sum of the remaining two angles is less than 90°.

Example 3. If the largest angle in a triangle measures 80°, what type of triangle might it be based on its angles?

Solution: Acute Triangle. because an acute triangle is a type of triangle in which all the three internal angles of the triangle are acute.

bit.ly/46Sw3rP

Find more at

Triangle Angle Sum

- One of the fundamental properties of a triangle is that the sum of its interior angles always equals 180°.

- Consider a triangle ABC.

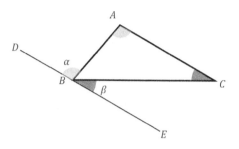

  - Draw a straight line DE parallel to side AC, passing through point B.

  - Angle α (between AB and DE) is equal to the angle at A (alternate angles due to parallel lines).

  - Similarly, angle β (between BC and DE) is equal to the angle at C.

  - Thus, the sum of the angles in triangle ABC is:

$$\angle A + \angle B + \angle C = \alpha + \angle B + \beta$$

Because $\alpha + \angle B + \beta$ forms a straight line, their sum is 180°. Hence, the angles in triangle ABC also sum up to 180°.

Examples:

Example 1. If two angles of a triangle measure 60° and 50°, what is the measure of the third angle?

Solution: Using the angle sum property:

Third angle $= 180° - (60° + 50°) = 180° - 110° = 70°$.

Example 2. A triangle has one angle that measures twice the sum of the other two angles. What are the measures of the angles?

Solution: Let the two smaller angles be $x°$ and $y°$. The larger angle is $2(x + y)°$. Using the angle sum property:

$$x° + y° + 2(x + y)° = 180° \rightarrow x° + y° = 60°$$

Without additional information about the relationship between $x°$ and $y°$, we have multiple solutions. For instance, $x°$ could be 30° and $y°$ could be 30°, or $x° = 20°$ and $y° = 40°$.

Triangle Midsegment

- A midsegment of a triangle is a segment that connects the midpoints of two sides of the triangle. Every triangle has three midsegments, and they have some interesting properties that are often discussed in geometry.

- Properties: Consider a triangle ABC, with D being the midpoint of AB, and E being the midpoint of AC.

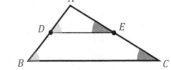

  - The midsegment is parallel to the third side of the triangle (the side not used to form the midsegment).

    Draw DE, the midsegment. Since D and E are midpoints, $AD = DB$ and $AE = EC$. By the Alternate Interior Angles Theorem (due to parallel lines cut by a transversal), DE is parallel to BC.

  - The length of the midsegment is half the length of the third side of the triangle.

    Consider triangles ADE and ABC. Since DE is parallel to BC and $AD = DB$, triangle ADE is similar to triangle ABC (by the AA criterion for similarity). Therefore, the sides are in proportion, and $DE = \frac{1}{2} \times BC$.

Examples:

Example 1. In triangle XYZ, M is the midpoint of side XY, and N is the midpoint of side XZ. If the length of side YZ is 14 units, what is the length of midsegment MN?

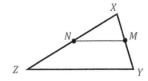

Solution: Using the properties of the midsegment:

$$MN = \frac{1}{2}YZ = \frac{1}{2}14 = 7 \ units$$

Example 2. In triangle PQR, if the midsegment connecting the midpoints of sides PQ and PR measures 9 units, what is the length of side QR?

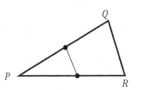

Solution: Using the properties of the midsegment:

$$QR = 2 \times midsegment = 2 \times 9 = 18 \ units$$

bit.ly/47bU7pu

Find more at

Angle Bisectors of Triangles

- An angle bisector in a triangle divides the given angle into two congruent angles. The properties of angle bisectors in triangles are:

  ▪ The angle bisector in a triangle divides the opposite side into two segments that are proportional to the other two sides of the triangle.

  Consider a triangle ABC, and let AD be the bisector of angle A, meeting side BC at D. By the Angle Bisector Theorem: $\frac{AB}{AC} = \frac{BD}{CD}$

  ▪ The incenter of a triangle is the point where all three angle bisectors meet. It's equidistant from all three sides of the triangle.

  ▪ The inradius, which is the radius of the incircle (a circle inscribed in the triangle), touches each side at a right angle.

  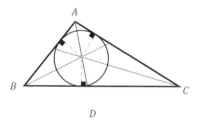

Examples:

Example 1. In triangle DEF, $DE = 6$ units, $DF = 8$ units, and DM is the angle bisector of angle D, meeting EF at M. If $MF = 4$ units, what is the length of ME?

Solution: Using the Angle Bisector Theorem: $\frac{DE}{DF} = \frac{ME}{MF}$

Plugging in the given values and simplifying, we get:
$$\frac{6}{8} = \frac{ME}{4} \rightarrow ME = \frac{6 \times 4}{8} \rightarrow ME = 3$$
Thus, $ME = 3$ units.

Example 2. In triangle GHI, $GH = 5$ units, $GI = 10$ units, and GN is the angle bisector of angle G, meeting HI at N. If $HN = x$ units, what is the length of IN in terms of x?

Solution: Using the Angle Bisector Theorem: $\frac{GH}{GI} = \frac{HN}{IN}$

Plugging in the given values and simplifying, we get:
$$\frac{5}{10} = \frac{x}{IN} \rightarrow IN = \frac{10x}{5} \rightarrow IN = 2x$$

Thus, $IN = 2x$ units.

Isosceles and Equilateral Triangles

- Isosceles and Equilateral Triangle special types of triangles have unique properties that distinguish them from other triangles.

   - Isosceles Triangle: An isosceles triangle has two sides of equal length. The angles opposite these equal sides are also congruent.

      - The angles opposite the equal sides are congruent.
      - The altitude drawn to the base (the side opposite the vertex angle) bisects the base and the vertex angle.

- Equilateral Triangle: An equilateral triangle has all its sides of equal length. As a result, all its angles are also equal.

   - All angles in an equilateral triangle measure 60°.
   - An altitude drawn in an equilateral triangle bisects the side it's drawn to and forms two $30° - 60° - 90°$ triangles.

Examples:

Example 1. In an isosceles triangle ABC, where $AB = AC$, if angle B is 50°, what is angle C?

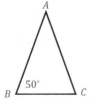

Solution: Since the triangle is isosceles and $AB = AC$, $\angle B = \angle C$.

Hence, angle C is also 50°.

Example 2. Triangle DEF is isosceles with $DE = DF$. If angle E is 40°, what is angle D?

Solution: Since angles E and F are congruent, angle F is 40°. Using the triangle angle sum property, $\angle D = 180° - 40° - 40° = 100°$.

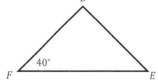

Example 3. If one side of an equilateral triangle is 6 units, what is the length of an altitude drawn to that side?

Solution: Drawing an altitude divides the triangle into two $30° - 60° - 90°$ triangles. The altitude becomes the longest side in this right triangle, so, the Pythagorean theorem applies:

$$a^2 + b^2 = c^2 \rightarrow a^2 + 3^2 = 6^2 \rightarrow a^2 = 36 - 9 \rightarrow a = \sqrt{27} \rightarrow a = 3\sqrt{3}$$

Therefore, the altitude is $3\sqrt{3}$ units.

bit.ly/3QKbd8I

Find more at

Right Triangles

- A right triangle is a triangle in which one of the angles is 90°. This type of triangle has unique properties and serves as a foundation for the Pythagorean theorem and trigonometry.

- Properties:

    ▪ Only one angle is 90°. This angle is called the right angle.

    ▪ The side opposite the right angle is the longest side and is called the hypotenuse.

    ▪ The Pythagorean theorem applies: $a^2 + b^2 = c^2$, where a and b are the lengths of the two shorter sides, and c is the length of the hypotenuse.

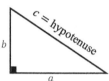

    ▪ Altitudes, medians, and angle bisectors drawn to the hypotenuse create two similar right triangles.

Examples:

Example 1. In a right triangle ABC, where angle C is 90°, if side $AC = 5$ units and side $BC = 12$ units, how long is side AB (the hypotenuse)?

Solution: Using the Pythagorean theorem:

$$AC^2 + BC^2 = AB^2 \rightarrow 5^2 + 12^2 = AB^2 \rightarrow 25 + 144 = AB^2 \rightarrow AB^2 = 169$$

$$\rightarrow AB = 13 \; units$$

Example 2. In a right triangle DEF, where angle E is 90°, if $DE = 8$ units and $EF = 15$ units, find the length of side DF.

Solution: Where is the angle E = 90°, DF is hypotenuse. Using the Pythagorean theorem:

$$DE^2 + EF^2 = DF^2 \rightarrow 8^2 + 15^2 = DF^2 \rightarrow 64 + 225 = DF^2 \rightarrow DF^2 = 289$$

$$\rightarrow DF = 17 \; units$$

Special Right Triangles

- A special right triangle is a triangle whose sides are in a particular ratio. Two special right triangles are $45° - 45° - 90°$ and $30° - 60° - 90°$ triangles.

- In a special $45° - 45° - 90°$ triangle, the three angles are $45°$, $45°$ and $90°$. The lengths of the sides of this triangle are in the ratio of $1: 1: \sqrt{2}$.

- In a special triangle $30° - 60° - 90°$, the three angles are $30° - 60° - 90°$. The lengths of this triangle are in the ratio of $1: \sqrt{3}: 2$.

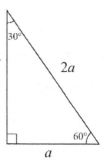

Examples:

Example 1. Find the length of the hypotenuse of a right triangle if the length of the other two sides are both 4 inches.

Solution: this is a right triangle with two equal sides. Therefore, it must be a $45° - 45° - 90°$ triangle. Two equivalent sides are 4 inches. The ratio of sides: $x: x: x\sqrt{2}$

The length of the hypotenuse is $4\sqrt{2}$ inches. $x: x: x\sqrt{2} \rightarrow 4: 4: 4\sqrt{2}$

Example 2. The length of the hypotenuse of a right triangle is 6 inches. What are the lengths of the other two sides if one angle of the triangle is $30°$?

Solution: The hypotenuse is 6 inches and the triangle is a $30° - 60° - 90°$ triangle. Then, one side of the triangle is 3 (it's half the side of the hypotenuse) and the other side is $3\sqrt{3}$. (it's the smallest side times $\sqrt{3}$)

$x: x\sqrt{3}: 2x \rightarrow x = 3 \rightarrow x: x\sqrt{3}: 2x = 3: 3\sqrt{3}: 6$

Example 3. Find the length of the hypotenuse of a right triangle if the length of the other two sides are both 6 inches.

Solution: this is a right triangle with two equal sides. Therefore, it must be a $45° - 45° - 90°$ triangle. Two equivalent sides are 6 inches. The ratio of sides: $x: x: x\sqrt{2}$

The length of the hypotenuse is $6\sqrt{2}$ inches. $x: x: x\sqrt{2} \rightarrow 6: 6: 6\sqrt{2}$

bit.ly/3xL9bJR

Find more at

The Pythagorean Theorem

- You can use the Pythagorean Theorem to find a missing side in a right triangle.

- In any right triangle: $a^2 + b^2 = c^2$

Examples:

Example 1. Right triangle ABC (not shown) has two legs of lengths $3\ cm$ (AB) and $4\ cm$ (AC). What is the length of the hypotenuse of the triangle (side BC)?

Solution: Use Pythagorean Theorem: $a^2 + b^2 = c^2$, $a = 3$, and $b = 4$

Then: $a^2 + b^2 = c^2 \rightarrow 3^2 + 4^2 = c^2 \rightarrow 9 + 16 = c^2 \rightarrow 25 = c^2 \rightarrow c = \sqrt{25} = 5$

The length of the hypotenuse is $5\ cm$.

Example 2. Find the hypotenuse of this triangle.

Solution: Use Pythagorean Theorem: $a^2 + b^2 = c^2$

Then: $a^2 + b^2 = c^2 \rightarrow 8^2 + 6^2 = c^2 \rightarrow 64 + 36 = c^2$

$c^2 = 100 \rightarrow c = \sqrt{100} = 10$

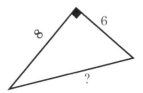

Example 3. Find the length of the missing side in this triangle.

Solution: Use Pythagorean Theorem: $a^2 + b^2 = c^2$

Then: $a^2 + b^2 = c^2 \rightarrow 12^2 + b^2 = 15^2 \rightarrow 144 + b^2 = 225 \rightarrow$

$\qquad b^2 = 225 - 144 \rightarrow b^2 = 81 \rightarrow b = \sqrt{81} = 9$

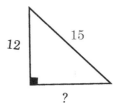

Example 4. Right triangle ABC (not shown) has two legs of lengths $8\ cm$ (AB) and $15\ cm$ (AC). What is the length of the hypotenuse of the triangle (side BC)?

Solution: Use Pythagorean Theorem: $a^2 + b^2 = c^2$, $a = 8$, and $b = 15$

Then: $a^2 + b^2 = c^2 \rightarrow 8^2 + 15^2 = c^2 \rightarrow 64 + 225 = c^2 \rightarrow 289 = c^2 \rightarrow c = \sqrt{289} = 17$

The length of the hypotenuse is $17\ cm$.

Pythagorean Theorem Converse: Is This a Right Triangle?

- The Pythagorean theorem converse is a mathematical statement that states that when the square on the largest edge of a triangle the same as the sum of squares of the two other sides, the triangle is a right triangle. With that said, the converse is derived from the Pythagorean theorem by using $[a]^2 + [b]^2 = [c]^2$.

- The converse of the Pythagorean Theorem is commonly employed in mathematical proofs that deal with triangles. It is also helpful in solving problems related to engineering and geometry. For instance, if you know the length of two sides of the triangle but not the third one, you could use the converse of the Pythagorean Theorem to determine the third. It is generally true that the converse of a theorem will be true only if, and only if, the original theorem is proved to be true. Thus, you can apply the converse from the Pythagorean Theorem to demonstrate that the triangle will be a right triangle only if the square of its longest side is the sum of squares of the two other sides.

Example:

A triangle has three sides of length 5 units, 12 units and 13 units. Using the Pythagorean converse theorem, determine whether this triangle is right-angled or not.

Solution: To solve this problem, you need to use the Pythagorean Theorem Converse, which states that if the sum of the squares of the two shorter sides of a triangle is equal to the square of the longest side, then the triangle is a right triangle.

In this case, the two shorter sides of the triangle are 5 units and 12 units, so we can square those values: $(5 \ units)^2 + (12 \ units)^2 = 25 + 144 = 169$

Now, we need to find the square of the hypotenuse, which is the longest side of the triangle: $c^2 = 13^2 = 169$

So, we can see that the sum of the squares of the two shorter sides of the triangle is equal to the square of the hypotenuse. Therefore, the triangle is a right triangle.

bit.ly/3PHX9fO

Geometric Mean in Triangles

- In a right triangle, if an altitude is drawn from the right angle to the hypotenuse, dividing the hypotenuse into two segments, then the length of the altitude is the geometric mean between the lengths of the two segments.

- if you have a right triangle ABC with the right angle at C and an altitude CD drawn to hypotenuse AB, dividing AB into segments AD and DB, then:
$CD^2 = AD \times DB$ and $CD = \sqrt{AD \times DB}$

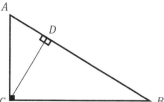

- Consider the right triangle ABC with altitude CD drawn to the hypotenuse AB. Triangle ADC and triangle BDC are similar to triangle ABC (AA similarity).

Using the ratios from the similar triangles: $\frac{AD}{AC} = \frac{AC}{AB} \rightarrow AD \times AB = AC^2$.

Similarly: $\frac{DB}{BC} = \frac{BC}{AB} \rightarrow DB \times AB = BC^2$

Adding both: $AD \times AB + DB \times AB = AC^2 + BC^2$

From the Pythagoras theorem, $AC^2 + BC^2 = AB^2 \rightarrow AD \times AB + DB \times AB = AB^2$. then. dividing both sides by AB, $AD + DB = AB$ (Which is true as AD and DB together make up the hypotenuse AB). And, since $CD^2 = AD \times D$, $CD = \sqrt{AD \times DB}$.

Example:

In a right triangle, the hypotenuse measures 16 units, and one of its segments after drawing an altitude from the right angle is 9 units. How long is the other segment, and what is the length of the altitude?

Solution: Let the length of the other segment be x.

Using the geometric mean property:

$$Altitude^2 = 9 \times x$$

Since the whole hypotenuse is 16 units, $x = 16 - 9 = 7$ units.

$$Altitude^2 = 9 \times 7$$

Altitude is $\sqrt{63}$ or $3\sqrt{7}$ units.

Exterior Angle Theorem

- The theorem of an exterior angle is a geometrical statement. It says that the measurement of the exterior angle will be the total of measurements involving two interior angles inside (which aren't adjacent). In other words, if you have a triangle and want to know the measurement of the angle that's not next to one of the other angles, you can take the sum of those two angles, which will give you your answer.

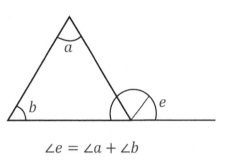

$$\angle e = \angle a + \angle b$$

- This theorem can be beneficial when solving for missing angles in a triangle. For example, if you know the measure of two angles in a triangle, you can use the exterior angle theorem to find the measure of the third angle. Additionally, this theorem can be used as a way to check whether or not a given triangle is valid. If the measures of the three angles in a triangle do not total 180 degrees, then the triangle is invalid.

- Take any exterior angle of a triangle (an angle formed by one triangle side and the extension of the adjacent side). The measure of that angle will equal the sum of the measures of the two interior angles that are not adjacent to it. This theorem can be applied to any triangle, as every triangle has three interior and exterior angles. Keep in mind that exterior angles are supplementary to their adjoining interior angle, forming a linear pair.

Example:

Find the value of x according to the figure.

Solution: To solve this problem, you can use the Exterior Angle Theorem, which states that the measure of an exterior angle of a triangle is equal to the sum of the measures of the remote interior angles.

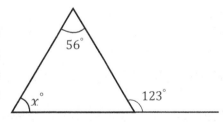

In this case, the exterior angle is 123 degrees and the remote interior angles are x and 56. So, using the theorem, we know that:

123 degrees $= x + 56 \rightarrow x = 123 - 56 = 67$

Medians

- A median of a triangle is a line segment that connects a vertex to the midpoint of the opposite side. Every triangle has three medians, and they possess some noteworthy properties and characteristics.

  ▪ The three medians of a triangle are concurrent, meaning they all meet at a single point. This point is called the centroid.

  ▪ The centroid divides each median into two segments, with the segment connecting the centroid to the triangle's vertex being twice as long as the segment connecting the centroid to the midpoint of the opposite side.

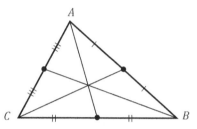

  ▪ The medians divide the triangle into six smaller triangles of equal area.

  ▪ The distance from a vertex to the centroid is $\frac{2}{3}$ the length of the median, and the distance from the centroid to the midpoint of the side opposite that vertex is $\frac{1}{3}$ the length of the median.

Examples:

Example 1. In triangle ABC, if AD is a median and $AD = 9$ units, how long are the segments from A to the centroid (let's call it G) and from G to D?

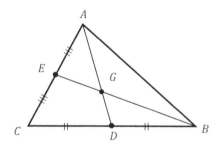

Solution: Using the properties of medians:

$AG = \frac{2}{3} \times AD = \frac{2}{3} \times 9 = 6$ units.

$GD = \frac{1}{3} \times AD = \frac{1}{3} \times 9 = 3$ units.

Example 2. If BE is another median of triangle ABC and its length is 12 units, what is the distance between vertex B and the centroid G?

Solution: Using the properties of medians:

$BG = \frac{2}{3} \times BE = \frac{2}{3} \times 12 = 8$ units.

Centroid

- The centroid of a triangle is the point where the triangle's three medians intersect. This point has some unique and significant properties:

  ▪ The centroid is the point of concurrency of the three medians of a triangle. This means all three medians meet at this single point.

  ▪ The centroid divides each median into two segments, where the segment from a vertex to the centroid is twice as long as the segment from the centroid to the midpoint of the opposite side. Mathematically, this is a $2:1$ ratio.

  ▪ The centroid is also the triangle's "center of mass." If you were to cut out a triangular piece of cardboard and balance it on a pin, it would balance at the centroid.

  ▪ The medians divide the triangle into six smaller triangles. Interestingly, all six of these triangles have the same area.

  ▪ If the coordinates of the vertices of a triangle in the coordinate plane are known, the centroid's coordinates (G_x, G_y) can be found using the average of the x −coordinates and the y-coordinates of the vertices:

$$G_x = \frac{A_x + B_x + C_x}{3}, \ G_y = \frac{A_y + B_y + C_y}{3}$$

Examples:

Example 1. Given triangle ABC with vertices $A(1,4)$, $B(5,10)$, and $C(7,2)$, find the coordinates of the centroid G.

Solution: Using the formula for finding the centroid's coordinates:

$$G_x = \frac{1+5+7}{3} = \frac{13}{3} = 4\frac{1}{3} \text{ and } G_y = \frac{4+10+2}{3} = \frac{16}{3} = 5\frac{1}{3}$$

Hence, the coordinates of G are $(4\frac{1}{3}, 5\frac{1}{3})$.

Example 2. In triangle XYZ, the medians from vertices X and Y intersect at point G. If XG is 12 units and GY is 9 units, how long is median YG?

Solution: Since the centroid divides the median in a $2:1$ ratio, the segment from Y to G is twice as long as the segment from G to the midpoint of side XZ.

Therefore, the length of YG is $\frac{1}{3}$ of the median's total length, making the total length of the median $3 \times 9 = 27$ units.

bit.ly/3QkQlDw

Find more at

The Triangle Inequality Theorem

- The Triangle Inequality Theorem describes a fundamental property regarding the lengths of the sides of a triangle. It states that the sum of the lengths of any two sides of a triangle must be greater than the length of the remaining side.

- **For any triangle _ABC_:** This theorem basically ensures that if you were to take any two sides of a triangle, they must be long enough, when added together, to surpass the third side. This is essential for the sides to meet and form a triangle.

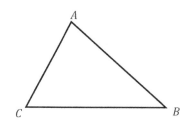

$$AB + BC > AC, BC + AC > AB, \text{ and } AC + AB > BC$$

Examples:

Example 1. Given two sides of a triangle measuring 5 units and 9 units, what range of lengths is possible for the third side?

Solution: Using the Triangle Inequality Theorem:

The sum of 5 and 9 is 14. So, the third side must be less than 14 units.

The difference between 5 and 9 is 4. So, the third side must be greater than 4 units.

Therefore, the third side can range from just over 4 units to just under 14 units.

Example 2. Is it possible to form a triangle with sides measuring 7 units, 10 units, and 18 units?

Solution: Using the Triangle Inequality Theorem:

$18 + 10 = 28$, which is greater than 7.
$7 + 18 = 25$, which is greater than 10.
$7 + 10 = 17$, which is less than 18, then it is not a triangle.

Since one of the combinations does not satisfy the theorem, a triangle cannot be formed with these side lengths.

SSS and SAS Congruence

- Triangle congruence refers to the conditions under which triangles are identical in all respects. There are several postulates that can be used to prove the congruence of triangles, among which the Side-Side-Side (SSS) and Side-Angle-Side (SAS) are two of the most commonly used.

  ▪ **Side-Side-Side (SSS) Congruence Postulate:** If the three sides of one triangle are congruent to the three sides of another triangle, then the two triangles are congruent.

  SSS

  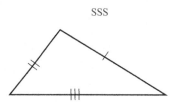

  ▪ **Side-Angle-Side (SAS) Congruence Postulate:** If two sides and the included angle of one triangle are congruent to two sides and the included angle of another triangle, then the triangles are congruent.

  SAS

  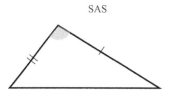

Examples:

Example 1. Given triangle ABC and triangle DEF with $AB = DE = 4\,cm$, $BC = EF = 6\,cm$, and $AC = DF = 5\,cm$, can we conclude the triangles are congruent?

Solution: Here, all three sides of triangle ABC are equal to the corresponding sides of triangle DEF. Hence, by the SSS congruence postulate, triangle ABC is congruent to triangle DEF.

Example 2. Given triangle PQR and triangle STU with $PQ = ST = 7\,cm$, $QR = TU = 8\,cm$, and $\angle PQR = \angle STU = 60°$, are the triangles congruent?

Solution: Here, two sides and the included angle of triangle PQR are equal to the corresponding sides and angle of triangle STU. Hence, by the SAS congruence postulate, triangle PQR is congruent to triangle STU.

bit.ly/3FFtzBl

Find more at

ASA and AAS Congruence

- Two postulates that help us determine the congruence of triangles based on their angles and sides are the Angle-Side-Angle (ASA) and Angle-Angle-Side (AAS) postulates.

   - **Angle-Side-Angle (ASA) Congruence Postulate:**
   If two angles and the included side of one triangle are congruent to two angles and the included side of another triangle, then the two triangles are congruent.

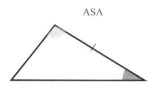

   - **Angle-Angle-Side (AAS) Congruence Postulate:**
   If two angles and a non-included side of one triangle are congruent to two angles and the corresponding non-included side of another triangle, then the two triangles are congruent.

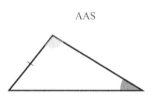

Examples:

Example 1. Given triangle XYZ and triangle LMN with $\angle X = \angle L$, angle $\angle Y = \angle M$, and $\overline{XY} = \overline{LM}$, can we conclude the triangles are congruent?

Solution: Here, the two angles and the included side of triangle XYZ are congruent to the corresponding angles and side of triangle LMN. Hence, by the ASA congruence postulate, triangle XYZ is congruent to triangle LMN.

Example 2. Given triangle RST and triangle UVW with $\angle R = \angle U$, $\angle T = \angle W$, and $\overline{RT} = \overline{UW}$, are the triangles congruent?

Solution: Two angles and the non-included side of triangle RST are congruent to the corresponding angles and side of triangle UVW. Hence, by the *AAS* congruence postulate, triangle RST is congruent to triangle UVW.

bit.ly/49gbBmr

Find more at

HL Congruences

- When we say two triangles are congruent, we mean that they are identical in shape and size. This means that their corresponding angles are equal, and their corresponding sides have the same lengths. We don't always need to know all the sides and angles of the triangles to determine if they are congruent.

- The fifth main postulates or theorems is:

    - **Hypotenuse-Leg (HL) Congruence:** Applicable to right triangles only. If the hypotenuse and one leg of a right triangle are congruent to the hypotenuse and one leg of another right triangle, then the triangles are congruent.

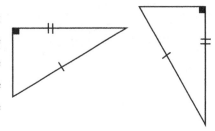

- These triangle congruence postulates and theorems serve as foundational tools for understanding the properties of triangles and solving problems related to triangle congruence in geometry.

Example:

Triangle ABC is a right triangle with hypotenuse $AC = 13\ cm$ and leg $AB = 5\ cm$. Triangle DEF is a right triangle with hypotenuse $DF = 13\ cm$ and leg $DE = 12\ cm$. can we conclude the triangles are congruent?

Solution: we cannot draw conclusions from this information. but, if we find another leg of triangle ABC or DEF, we can see if they are congruent.

Use Pythagorean Theorem for triangle ABC: $AB^2 + BC^2 = AC^2$, $AB = 5$, and $AC = 13$

Then: $AB^2 + BC^2 = AC^2 \rightarrow 5^2 + BC^2 = 13^2 \rightarrow 25 + BC^2 = 169 \rightarrow BC = \sqrt{169 - 25} \rightarrow BC = 12$ The length of the BC is $12\ cm$.

Hance, the hypotenuse and leg DE of triangle DEF are congruent to the corresponding hypotenuse and leg BC of triangle ABC. Hence, by the HL congruence postulate, triangle ABC is congruent to triangle DEF.

Chapter 6: Practices

✎ Find the measure of the unknown angle in each triangle.

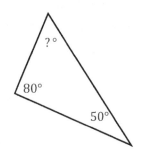

1)

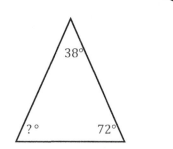

3)

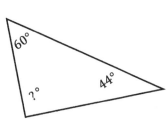

2)

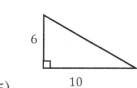

4)

✎ Find the area of each triangle.

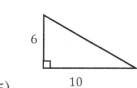

5)

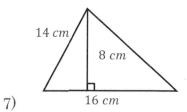

7)

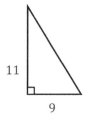

6)

8)

✍ **Classify each triangle by each angle and sides. Base your decision on the actual lengths of the sides and the measures of the angles.**

9)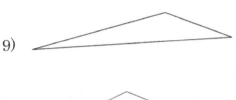

11)

10)

12)

✍ **Classify each triangle by angles and sides.**

13)

15)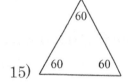

14)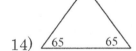

16)

✍ **Find the measure of each angle indicated.**

17)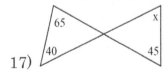

20)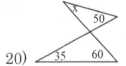

18)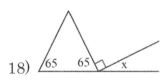

21)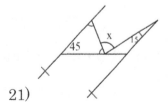

19)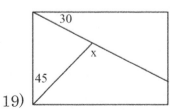

22)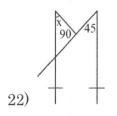

Effortless Math Education

✍ **Solve for *x*.**

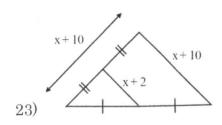

23)

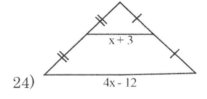

24)

✍ **Find the missing length indicated.**

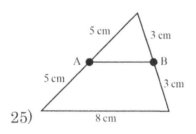

25)

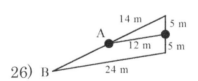

26) B

✍ **In the following triangle, *M*, *N* and *P* are the midpoints of the sides. Name a segment parallel to the one given.**

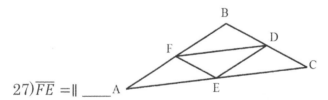

27) $\overline{FE}$ = ‖ _____

✍ **For each triangle, construct the angle bisector of angle *A*.**

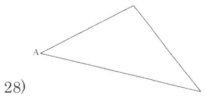

28)

29)

✍ **Locate the incenter of each triangle.**

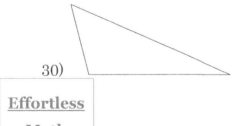

30)

31)

✍ **For each triangle, construct all three angle bisectors to show they are concurrent.**

32)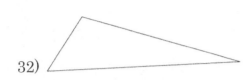

33)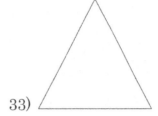

✍ **Find the value of *x*.**

34)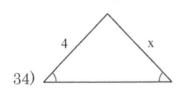

38)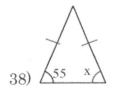

35)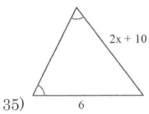

39)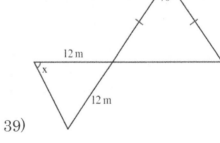

36)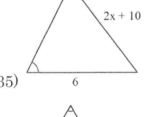

40)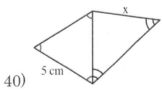

37)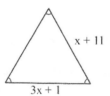

41)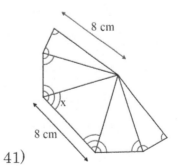

✎ **Find the missing side. Round to the nearest tenth.**

42)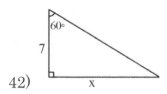

47)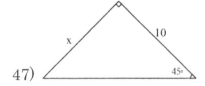

43)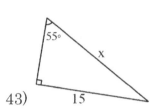

48)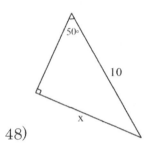

44)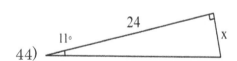

49)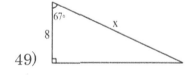

45)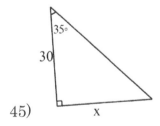

50)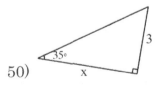

46)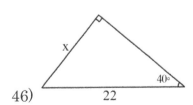

51)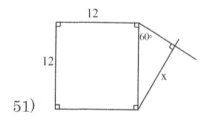

Effortless

Math

Education

✎ Solve

52) If one of the acute angles in a right triangle is 45°, and the length of the hypotenuse is $10\sqrt{2}$ units, what are the lengths of the other two sides?

53) A right triangle has one leg that measures 5 units, and the two acute angles measure 30° and 60°, respectively. What are the lengths of the hypotenuse and the other leg?

54) In a right triangle with angles of 45, 45, and 90 degrees, the length of one leg is "a" units. Express the lengths of the hypotenuse and the other leg in terms of "a".

55) The length of the hypotenuse of a right triangle is 12 inches. What are the lengths of the other two sides if one angle of the triangle is 60°?

✎ Find the missing side lengths. Leave your answers as radicals in simplest form.

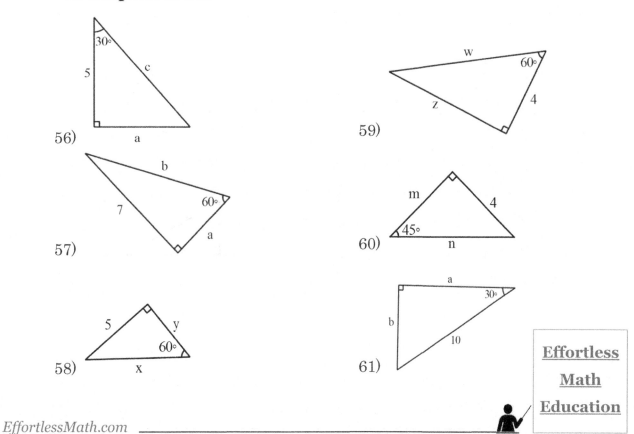

56)

57)

58)

59)

60)

61)

Effortless Math Education

✑ **Find the missing side lengths. Leave your answers as radicals in simplest form.**

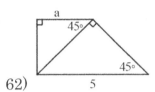

62)

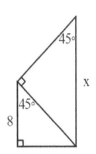

63)

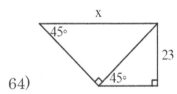

64)

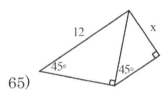

65)

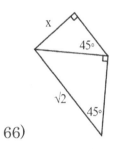

66)

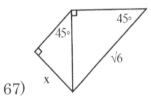

67)

✑ **Find the missing side?**

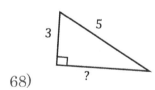

68)

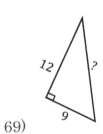

69)

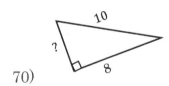

70)

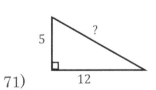

71)

✎ Find

72) Determine the type of triangle formed by the sides with lengths $9\ cm, 14\ cm$, and $15\ cm$, using the Pythagorean converse theorem.

73) Given a triangle with sides of length $7\ cm, 24\ cm$, and $27\ cm$, determine whether the triangle is right-angled or not using the Pythagorean converse theorem.

74) A triangle has sides of length $8\ cm, 15\ cm$, and $17\ cm$. Determine whether this triangle is right-angled or not using the Pythagorean converse theorem.

75) A triangle has sides of length $6\ cm, 8\ cm$, and $10\ cm$. Determine whether this triangle is right-angled or not using the Pythagorean converse theorem.

✎ Find the value of x. Round to the nearest tenth.

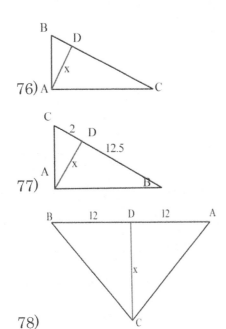

76)

77)

78)

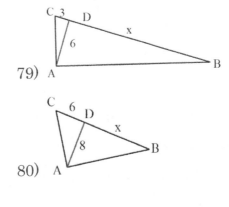

79)

80)

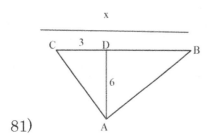

81)

🖎 **Solve for** *x*.

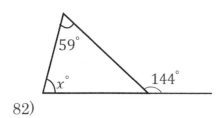

82)

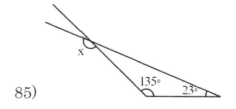

85)

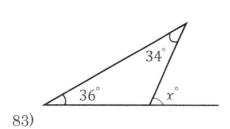

83)

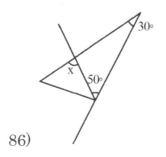

86)

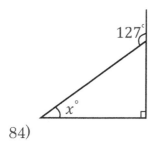

84)

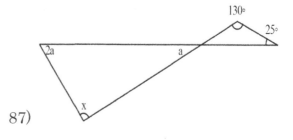

87)

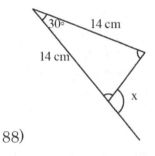

88)

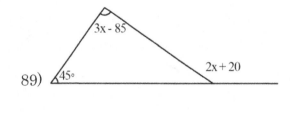

89)

🖎 **Each figure shows a triangle with one or more of its medians.**

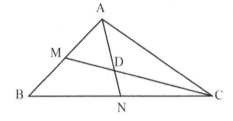

90) Find DM if $CM = 6.6$

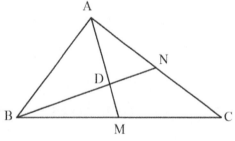

93) Find x if $BN = 6x - 9$ and $DN = x$

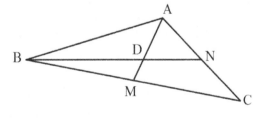

91) Find AD if $AM = 4.5$

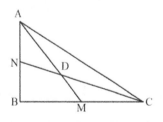

94) Find CD if $DN = 6x$ and $CN = 15x + 6$

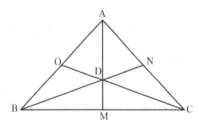

92) Find AD if $DM = 5$

95) Find $AD + ND$ if $BD = 4$ and $DM = 2$

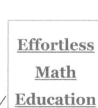

Effortless
Math
Education

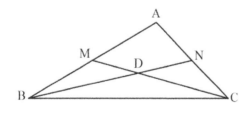 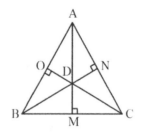

96) Find x if $BN = 6x - 3$ and $DN = x + 7$

97) Find DM if $DN = 6$ and $AN = 8$

✏️ **Find the coordinates of the centroid of each triangle given the three vertices.**

98) $Y(1, -4), X(2, 10), W(2, -1)$

100) $S(1, 2), R(-1, 6), Q(2, 3)$

99) $T(2, -1), U(3, 3), V(1, 4)$

101) $E(2, -9), D(5, 0), C(1, -1)$

✏️ **Find coordinates of the centroid of each triangle.**

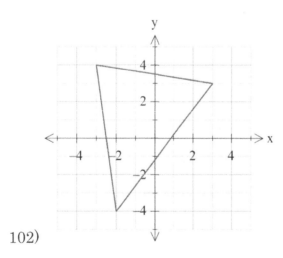

102)

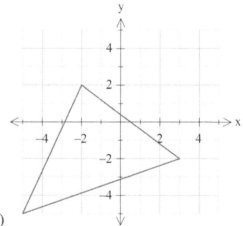

103)

✏️ **Two sides of a triangle have the following measures. Find the range of possible measures for the third side.**

104) $4, 10$

106) $16, 25$

108) $13, 20$

105) $16, 4$

107) $1, 3$

109) $8, 11$

Effortless

Math

Education

✏ **State if the three numbers can be the measures of the sides of a triangle.**

110) $3, 5, 13$ 113) $4, 12, 8$ 116) $1, 5, 5$

111) $8, 11, 9$ 114) $3, 3, 3$ 117) $4, 7, 2$

112) $3, 9, 8$ 115) $3, 9, 8$ 118) $15, 21, 7$

✏ **State what additional information is required in order to know that the triangles are congruent for the reason given.**

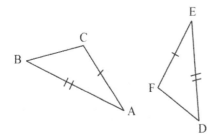

119) SSS

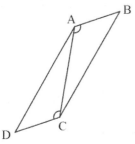

120) AAS

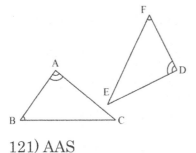

121) AAS

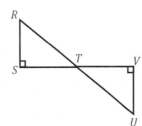

122) SAS

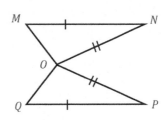

123) ASA

124) SAS

Effortless
Math
Education

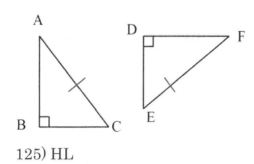

125) HL

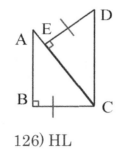

126) HL

Chapter 6: Answers

1) 50

2) 76

3) 84

4) 70

5) 30

6) 49.5

7) 64 cm^2

8) 90 in^2

9) Obtuse scalene

10) Obtuse isosceles

11) Right scalene

12) Acute isosceles

13) Right scalene

14) Acute isosceles

15) Equilateral

16) Obtuse isosceles

17) 60°

18) 25°

19) 105°

20) 55°

21) 82.5°

22) 45°

23) 6

24) 9

25) 4 cm

26) 14 cm

27) $\overline{BC}$

28)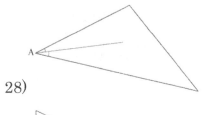

29)

30)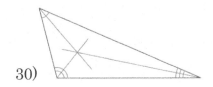

31)

32)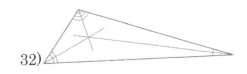

33)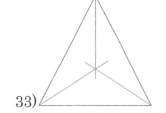

34) 4

35) -2

36) 5

37) 36°

38) 55°

39) 62.5°

40) 5 cm

41) 60°

42) 12.1

43) 18.3

44) 4.7

45) 21

46) 14.1

47) 10

48) 7.7

49) 20.5

50) 4.3

51) 10.4

52) 10

53) 10, $5\sqrt{3}$

54) $a\sqrt{2}$

55) 6, $6\sqrt{3}$

56) $c = 10\frac{\sqrt{3}}{3}, a = 5\frac{\sqrt{3}}{3}$

57) $a = \frac{7}{\sqrt{3}}, b = \frac{14}{\sqrt{3}}$

58) $x = \frac{10}{\sqrt{3}}, y = \frac{5}{\sqrt{3}}$

59) $x = 4\sqrt{3}, y = 8$

60) $m = 4, n = 4\sqrt{2}$

61) $a = \frac{15}{\sqrt{3}}, b = 5$

62) 2.5

63) 16

64) 46

65) 6

66) $\frac{\sqrt{2}}{2}$

67) $\frac{\sqrt{6}}{2}$

68) 4

69) 15

70) 6

71) 13

72) The triangle is not a right triangle.

73) The triangle is not a right triangle.

74) The triangle is a right triangle.

75) The triangle is a right triangle.

76) $x = \sqrt{BD \times CD}$

77) 5

78) 12

79) 12

80) $\sqrt{28} \approx 5.3$

81) 8.2

82) 85

83) 70

84) 37

85) 158°

86) 80°

87) 105°

Effortless Math Education

88) $105°$

89) 60

90) 2.2

91) 3

92) 10

93) 3

94) 24

95) 6

96) 8

97) 5

98) $(\frac{5}{3}, \frac{5}{3})$

99) $(2, 2)$

100) $(\frac{2}{3}, \frac{11}{3})$

101) $(\frac{8}{3}, -\frac{10}{3})$

102) $(-\frac{2}{3}, 1)$

103) $(-\frac{4}{3}, -\frac{5}{3})$

104) $6 < x < 14$

105) $12 < x < 20$

106) $2 < x < 4$

107) $3 < x < 19$

108) $7 < x < 33$

109) $3 < x < 19$

110) No

111) Yes

112) Yes

113) No

114) Yes

115) Yes

116) Yes

117) No

118) Yes

119) $\overline{BC} = \overline{FD}$

120) $\angle B = \angle D$

121) $\overline{DE} = \overline{AC}$
    or $\overline{FE} = \overline{BC}$

122) $\overline{WZ} = \overline{XY}$

123) $\overline{ST} = \overline{TV}$

124) $\angle N = \angle P$

125) $\overline{AB} = \overline{FD}$
    or $\overline{BC} = \overline{DE}$

126) $\overline{DC} = \overline{AC}$

Effortless
Math
Education

CHAPTER

7 Dilation and Similarity

Math topics that you'll learn in this chapter:

☑ Dilations

☑ Dilations and Angles

☑ Similarity

☑ Similarity Criteria

☑ Congruent and Similar Figures

☑ Area and Perimeter: Scale Changes

☑ The Side Splitter Theorem

☑ Similarity Transformations

☑ Partitioning a Line Segment

☑ Similar Polygons

☑ Right Triangles and Similarity

☑ Similar Solids

165

Dilations

- Dilation is a transformation in geometry that changes the size of a figure without altering its shape. It can either enlarge or reduce the figure based on a scale factor and a center of dilation.

- **Center of Dilation:** The fixed point in the plane about which the figure is dilated.

- **Scale Factor** (k): The ratio by which a figure is enlarged or reduced.
    - If $k > 1$, the dilation is an enlargement.
    - If $0 < k < 1$, the dilation is a reduction.
    - If $k = 1$, the figure remains unchanged.

- Properties:

    - Dilations preserve the shape but not necessarily the size.

    - Angle measures remain unchanged in dilation.

    - The lengths of the sides are multiplied by the scale factor.

    - The area of a 2 −dimensional figure is multiplied by k^2.

    - For 3 −dimensional figures, the volume is multiplied by k^3.

Examples:

Example 1. If a rectangle with dimensions 4 *cm* by 6 *cm* undergoes a dilation with a scale factor of 3, what are the new dimensions of the rectangle?

Solution: To find the new dimensions of the rectangle, you must multiply each side by the scale factor of 3.

The new length is $4 \times 3 = 12$ *cm*.

The new width is $6 \times 3 = 18$ *cm*.

Example 2. A triangle has an area of 50 square units. If it undergoes a dilation with a scale factor of 0.5, what will be the area of the dilated triangle?

Solution: To find the new area of the triangle, you must multiply the area by the scale factor to the power of 2.

New area = Original area $\times k^2 = 50 \times 0.5^2 = 50 \times 0.25 = 12.5$ square units.

bit.ly/49m3xQY

Find more at

Dilations and Angles

- The effects of dilations on Angles are:

  ▪ **Angle Measures Remain Unchanged**: A significant property of dilations is that they preserve angles. Whether a figure is enlarged or reduced, the angle measures remain the same in the pre-image and the image. This is because dilation maintains the figure's shape, even if its size changes.

  ▪ **Parallel Lines:** When a polygon is dilated, any set of parallel sides in the original polygon (pre-image) will remain parallel in the dilated figure (image). This preservation of parallelism ensures that corresponding angles between these parallel lines (created by transversals) remain congruent, further emphasizing that angles are preserved under dilations.

- Why are angles preserved? Consider two lines that form an angle and intersect at the center of dilation. As these lines are dilated, they move outward or inward, maintaining the same angle of intersection. Lines not passing through the center of dilation will still retain their orientation to each other, ensuring that their angle of intersection remains unchanged.

Examples:

Example 1. If a triangle with angles measuring 40°, 75°, and 65° undergoes a dilation with a scale factor of 2.5, what are the angles of the dilated triangle?

Solution: The angles remain unchanged under dilation. Therefore, the angles of the dilated triangle are still 40°, 75°, and 65°.

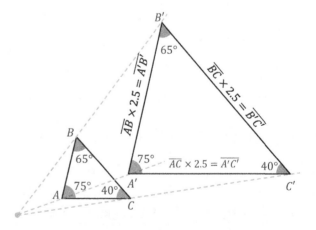

Example 2. A parallelogram has angles measuring 80° and 100°. If it undergoes a dilation with a scale factor of 0.7, what will be the angles of the dilated parallelogram?

Solution: The angles of the parallelogram will remain 80° and 100°, regardless of the dilation.

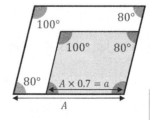

Find more at

Similarity

- Dilation is a transformation that produces a figure similar to the original by shrinking or enlarging it.

- In geometry, similarity refers to the relationship between two shapes that have the same form or structure but may differ in size. Figures that are similar maintain the same shape but can have different side lengths. However, their corresponding angles are congruent.

- The properties of Similar Figures are:

  - **Corresponding Angles:** In similar figures, the corresponding angles are congruent.

  - **Proportional Sides:** The lengths of corresponding sides in similar figures are proportional.

Examples:

Example 1. Two triangles have side lengths in the ratio of $3:5$. If the smallest side of the first triangle is 6 cm, how long is the smallest side of the second triangle?

Solution: Using the given ratio, if the side of the first triangle is $3x$, then $3x = 6\ cm$, which means $x = 2\ cm$. For the second triangle, the side will be $5x$, making it 10 cm.

Example 2. In two similar rectangles, the ratio of their lengths is $4:7$. If the width of the smaller rectangle is 8 cm, find the length of the larger rectangle given that its length is 3 times its width.

Solution: The length of the smaller rectangle is 3 times its width, so it's $3 \times 8\ cm = 24\ cm$. Then, the length of the smaller rectangle is $4x$, then $4x = 24\ cm$, which means $x = 6\ cm$. For the larger rectangle, the length will be $7x$, making it $7 \times 6 = 42\ cm$.

bit.ly/3tRnUFs

Find more at

Similarity Criteria

- Unlike congruence, where the triangles are the exact same size and shape, similarity only concerns the shape. Two triangles are similar if they have the same shape but not necessarily the same size.

- Criteria for Triangle Similarity:

  - **AA (Angle-Angle) Similarity:** If two angles of one triangle are congruent to two angles of another triangle, then the triangles are similar. Because the sum of angles in any triangle is always 180°, so if two angles are congruent, the third angle will be automatically congruent as well.

  - **SAS (Side-Angle-Side) Similarity:** If the ratio of the lengths of two sides in one triangle is equal to the ratio of the lengths of two corresponding sides in another triangle, and the angles included between these sides are congruent, then the triangles are similar.

  - **SSS (Side-Side-Side) Similarity:** If the ratios of the lengths of three pairs of corresponding sides of two triangles are equal, then the triangles are similar.

Examples:

Example 1. Triangle ABC has angles measuring 40°, 50°, and 90°. Triangle DEF has angles measuring 50°, 40°, and 90°. Are the two triangles similar?

Solution: Using the AA criterion, since two angles (50° and 40°) of triangle ABC are congruent to two angles of triangle DEF, the two triangles are similar.

Example 2. In triangles PQR and XYZ, $\frac{PQ}{XY} = \frac{4}{5}$, $\frac{QR}{YZ} = \frac{4}{5}$, and $\angle PQR = \angle XYZ$. Are the triangles similar?

Solution: The side ratios are proportional, and the included angles are congruent, so by the SAS criterion, triangles PQR and XYZ are similar.

For triangles MNO and UVW, $\frac{MN}{UV} = \frac{3}{6}$, $\frac{NO}{VW} = \frac{4}{8}$, and $\frac{MO}{UW} = \frac{5}{10}$. Are the triangles similar?

Solution: All side ratios simplify to $\frac{1}{2}$. Thus, by the SSS criterion, triangles MNO and UVW are similar.

bit.ly/3SpaJG5

Find more at

Congruent and Similar Figures

Similar VS Congruent

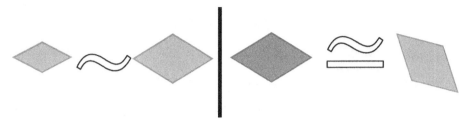

- In geometry, two figures are said to be congruent if one can be translated, rotated, or reflected to fit onto the other perfectly. This means they have the exact same size, lengths, and angles. Congruent figures are often used in engineering and construction, as they can be easily interchanged without affecting the overall design. On the other hand, similar figures have the same proportions and shape, yet are not the exact same size. While similar figures can be used in some instances, they are not as versatile as congruent figures and are less commonly used.

Examples:

Example 1. Are the two following triangles congruent?

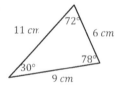
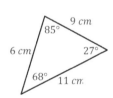

Solution: The angles of the two triangles are completely different, so the two triangles are not congruent.

Example 2. Are the two following rectangles similar?

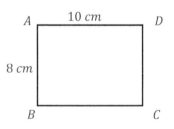

Solution: All the angles of the rectangles are 90 degrees, so the angles of the two shapes are the same. Now calculate the ratio of the corresponding sides of the two rectangles:

The ratio of side EF to side $AB = \frac{12}{8} = \frac{3}{2}$

The ratio of side FG to side $BC = \frac{12}{8} = \frac{3}{2}$

The ratio of side GH to side $CD = \frac{12}{8} = \frac{3}{2}$

The ratio of side HE to side $DA = \frac{12}{8} = \frac{3}{2}$

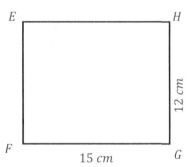

Given that the angles are equal, and the sides are proportional, the two rectangles are similar.

Area and Perimeter: Scale Changes

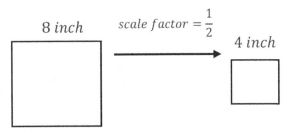

- The scale factor allows us to change a figure's size without modifying the shape. In other words, if we want to make a smaller or larger figure, we can use the scale factor. A scale factor is a number we use to multiply the initial figure's dimensions to get the new figure's dimensions. So, for example, if we have a square with sides that are each 8 inches long, and we want to create a new square that is half the original square's size, our scale factor would be $\frac{1}{2}$. We would multiply each dimension of the initial square by $\frac{1}{2}$, giving us our new square's dimensions.

- The formula to determine a figure's scale factor is as follows:

    Scale factor = New shape's dimensions ÷ Original shape's dimensions

Example:

The length and width of a rectangle are equal to 7 and 4 units, respectively. These dimensions increase by a factor of 3. What is the length, width, perimeter and area of the new rectangle?

Solution: When the scale of a figure is increased by a factor of n, the size of the length and width of the figure is multiplied by n.

Therefore, the dimensions of the new shape are obtained using the above formula:

the new length of the rectangle: $7\ units \times 3 = 21\ units$

the new width of the rectangle: $4\ units \times 3 = 12\ units$

By adding the length of the sides of the new rectangle, its perimeter is obtained:

$$(2 \times 21) + (2 \times 12) = 42 + 24 = 66\ units$$

The area of a rectangle is obtained by multiplying the length by the width, so the new area will be: $21 \times 12 = 252\ square\ units$

The new dimensions of the rectangle are 21 units by 12 units, the new perimeter is 66 units and the new area is 252 square units.

Find more at
bit.ly/3pxl1ba

The Side Splitter Theorem

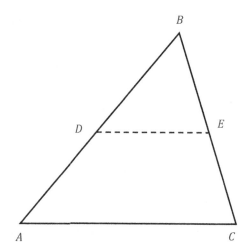

- The Side Splitter Theorem is an essential concept in geometry, especially when dealing with triangles and lines that cut, or "split" their sides.

- If a line (or segment) is parallel to one side of a triangle and intersects the other two sides, then it divides those sides proportionally.

- Formally, consider a triangle ABC with a line segment DE that's parallel to side AC and intersects side AB at point D and side BC at point E. Then, according to the Side Splitter Theorem:

$$\frac{BD}{DA} = \frac{BE}{EC}$$

Example:

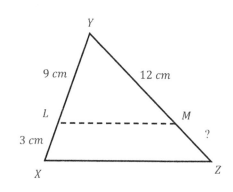

In triangle XYZ, line segment LM is drawn parallel to side XZ, intersecting side XY at L and side YZ at M. If $XL = 3\ cm$, $LY = 9\ cm$, and $YM = 12\ cm$, find the length of MZ.

Solution: According to the Side Splitter Theorem:

$$\frac{XL}{LY} = \frac{YM}{MZ}$$

Plugging in the known values:

$$\frac{3}{9} = \frac{12}{MZ} \rightarrow \frac{1}{3} = \frac{12}{MZ} \rightarrow MZ = 36$$

Thus, the length of MZ is $36\ cm$.

bit.ly/3SsMBCr

Find more at

Similarity Transformations

- When transformations preserve the shape (but not necessarily the size) of a figure, they are called similarity transformations. These transformations can change the position, size, and orientation of the figure but not its shape.

- Types of Similarity Transformations:

    - **Translation:** Every point of the figure moves the same distance in the same direction.
    - **Reflection:** A reflection "flips" a figure over a line, called the line of reflection. The figure and its image are mirror images of each other.
    - **Rotation:** A rotation turns a figure about a fixed point, called the center of rotation.
    - **Dilation:** A dilation resizes a figure by a scale factor relative to a fixed point, called the center of dilation.

- Properties of Similarity Transformations:

    - They produce an image that is similar to the original figure.

    - The measures of corresponding angles remain the same.

    - The lengths of corresponding sides change by the same scale factor (except for translations, reflections, and rotations where the size remains unchanged).

Examples:

Example 1. A triangle with vertices $A(2, 3)$, $B(5, 7)$, and $C(6, 2)$ is translated 3 units right and 2 units up. What are the coordinates of the image triangle $A'B'C'$?

Solution: Move each vertex in $x = +3$ and $y = +2$ directions.

$$A'(2 + 3, 3 + 2) = A'(5, 5)$$
$$B'(5 + 3, 7 + 2) = B'(8, 9)$$
$$C'(6 + 3, 2 + 2) = C'(9, 4)$$

Example 2. A rectangle is dilated from a center of dilation at its bottom-left vertex with a scale factor of 0.5. If the original rectangle had a length of 8 units and width of 6 units, what are the dimensions of the dilated rectangle?

Solution: To find the dimensions of the new rectangle, you must multiply each side by the scale factor:

Length: $8 \times 0.5 = 4$ units
Width: $6 \times 0.5 = 3$ units6

bit.ly/461RGES

Find more at

Partitioning a Line Segment

- Partitioning a line segment means dividing it into two or more segments, often in a specific ratio. This concept is frequently used in geometry to find an exact point on a segment based on a given ratio.

- Given a line segment AB and a ratio of $m{:}n$, the coordinates (x, y) of the point P that partitions the segment in the given ratio is calculated as:

$$x = \frac{mx_2 + nx_1}{m+n}, \; y = \frac{mY_2 + ny_1}{m+n}$$

Where $A(x_1, y_1)$ and $B(x_2, y_2)$ are the endpoints of the segment.

- Steps to Partition a Line Segment:

  ▪ Identify the endpoints of the line segment and their coordinates.

  ▪ Determine the desired ratio for partitioning the segment.

  ▪ Use the formula to find the x and y coordinates of the partition point.

Examples:

Example 1. Divide the line segment with endpoints $A(1, 2)$ and $B(7, 8)$ in the ratio $2{:}3$. What are the coordinates of the point that partitions the segment?

Solution: Using the formula, we find the $x-$coordinate as: $x = \frac{2(7)+3(1)}{2+3} = 3.4$

And the $y-$coordinate as: $y = \frac{2(8)+3(2)}{2+3} = \frac{22}{5} = 4.4$

Thus, the partition point is $P(3.4, 4.4)$.

Example 2. A line segment has endpoints $C(2, 5)$ and $D(8, 9)$. Find the coordinates of the point that divides CD in the ratio $1{:}4$.

Solution: For the $x-$coordinate: $x = \frac{1(8)+4(2)}{1+4} = \frac{16}{5} = 3.2$

For the $y-$coordinate: $y = \frac{1(9)+4(5)}{1+4} = \frac{29}{5} = 5.8$

The partition point is $E(3.2, 5.8)$.

Similar Polygons

- Two polygons are similar if their corresponding angles are congruent, and the ratios of the lengths of their corresponding sides are equal.

- Properties of Similar Polygons

  - **Corresponding Angles are Congruent:** If two polygons are similar, then their corresponding angles are equal.
  - **Sides are Proportional:** The ratio of the lengths of corresponding sides of the two polygons is constant. If $ABCD$ is similar to $WXYZ$, and the ratio of side AB to WX is k, then the ratios of $BC:XY$, $CD:YZ$, and $DA:ZW$ will all also be k.

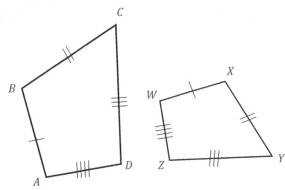

- The symbol "~" denotes similarity. If polygon $ABCD$ is similar to polygon $WXYZ$, we write it as $ABCD \sim WXYZ$.

- For two polygons to be similar:

  - They must have the same number of sides.
  - The angles of one polygon should be congruent to the corresponding angles of the other polygon.
  - The sides of one polygon should be proportional to the corresponding sides of the other polygon.

Example:

Quadrilateral $GHIJ$ is similar to quadrilateral MNOP. If the ratio of their corresponding sides is $3:4$, and $GH = 9\ cm$, what is the length of side MN?

Solution: Using the given ratio, if GH is $3x$, then $3x = 9\ cm$, which means $x = 3\ cm$. For MN, the side will be $4x$, making it $12\ cm$.

bit.ly/3FHiwaD

Find more at

Right Triangles and Similarity

- Right triangles are triangles with one angle measuring 90°. When an altitude is drawn from the right angle of a right triangle to its hypotenuse, it creates two smaller right triangles. These triangles are similar to each other and to the original triangle. This is because they all share the same angles.

- Properties Resulting from Altitude to the Hypotenuse:

- **Three Similar Triangles:** Triangle ABC (Original triangle), triangle DBA (Smaller triangle including the altitude), and triangle DAC (Other smaller triangle) are all similar.

- **Proportional Sides:** The segments of the hypotenuse, created by the altitude, are proportional to the legs of the right triangle. For instance, if AD is an altitude from A to hypotenuse BC in triangle ABC, then $\frac{BD}{AB} = \frac{AB}{BC}$ and $\frac{DC}{AC} = \frac{AC}{BC}$.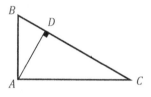

- **Area Relationship:** The area of triangle ABC is equal to the sum of the areas of triangles DBA and DAC.

- Geometric Mean: The altitude to the hypotenuse of a right triangle has a special relationship with the two segments it divides the hypotenuse into:

  If h is the altitude and x and y are the segments of the hypotenuse, then $h^2 = x \times y$.

Examples:

Example 1. A right triangle has legs of $6\ cm$ and $8\ cm$. If an altitude is drawn from the right angle to the hypotenuse, dividing the hypotenuse into segments of $3.6\ cm$ and $10.4\ cm$, verify that these segments are proportional to the triangle's legs.

Solution: The ratio of the hypotenuse segment to the corresponding leg is $\frac{3.6}{6} = 0.6$ and $\frac{10.4}{8} = 1.3$. Since these ratios are not equal, they aren't proportional.

Example 2. For a right triangle with hypotenuse segments of $9\ cm$ and $16\ cm$ formed by an altitude, determine the length of the altitude using the geometric mean relationship.

Solution: Using the geometric mean relationship:

$$h^2 = 9 \times 16 \rightarrow h^2 = 144 \rightarrow h = 12\ cm$$

Similar Solids

- There are times when it can be helpful to know if two objects are similar, and other times when the difference in size is what matters. To identify similar objects, it's important first to understand what that means. Two objects are similar if they have the exact same shape, yet do not have the exact same size. As such, corresponding segments will be proportional, while corresponding faces will be similar polygons. There are four steps involved in determining whether two solids are similar:

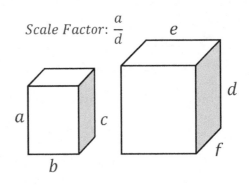

Scale Factor: $\frac{a}{d}$

- First, determine corresponding dimensions.

- Second, the ratio of lengths for corresponding dimensions must be found.

- Third, check if all the ratios happen to be the same. The solids will be similar if they are.

- Fourth, if solids happen to be similar, then you can find the scale factor. So, for example, if a solid is twice as big as another solid, then the scale factor is 2.

Example:

Two rectangular prisms are similar. What is the volume of the larger prisms?

Solution: To calculate the volume of the larger cube, you must first find the value of x. Given that the two figures are similar, use the two corresponding pairs of sides to form the proportion and find x:

$\frac{4}{2} = \frac{x}{6} \rightarrow 2x = 24 \rightarrow x = 12$

Now calculate the volume:

$V = 6 \times 4 \times 12 = 288$

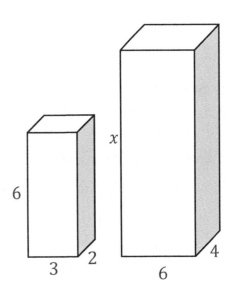

bit.ly/3JLdYm3

Find more at

Chapter 7: Practices

✍ **Solve.**

1) A rectangle has a length of 8 units and a width of 6 units. If the rectangle is dilated by a scale factor of 3, what will be the length and width of the resulting rectangle?

2) A triangle has sides measuring 7 units, 10 units, and 12 units. If the triangle is dilated by a scale factor of 0.5, what will be the length of each side of the resulting triangle?

3) The diagram shows two concentric circles with radii labeled as follows: What is the scale factor of Circle B relative to Circle A?

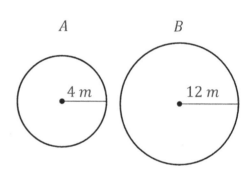

4) A hexagon has an area of 120 square centimeters. If it undergoes a dilation with a scale factor of 0.25, what will be the area of the dilated hexagon?

✍ **Solve.**

5) A rhombus has angles measuring 60° and 120°. If it undergoes a dilation with a scale factor of 2, what will be the angles of the dilated rhombus? Also, if the original rhombus had a side length of 5 *cm*, what will be the side length of the dilated rhombus?

6) A trapezoid has angles measuring 60°, 120°, 60°, and 120°. If it undergoes a dilation with a scale factor of 1.5, what will be the angles of the dilated trapezoid?

✏️ **State if the polygons are similar.**

7)

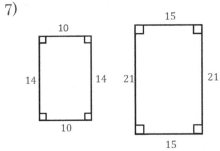

9)

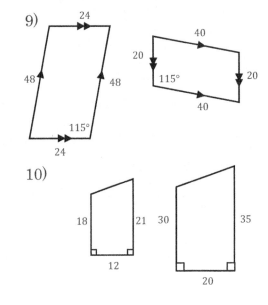

8)

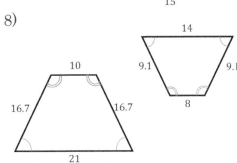

10)

✏️ **State**

11) Two similar triangles have a ratio of their corresponding sides as $3:5$. If the shortest side of the larger triangle is $15\ cm$, find the length of the shortest side of the smaller triangle. Also, find the length of the longest side of the larger triangle if it is twice the length of its shortest side.

12) In two similar pentagons, the ratio of their corresponding sides is $2:3$. If the perimeter of the smaller pentagon is $30\ cm$, find the perimeter of the larger pentagon. Additionally, if the longest side of the smaller pentagon is $8\ cm$, what is the length of the longest side of the larger pentagon?

13) Two similar circles have a ratio of their radii as $5:8$. If the circumference of the smaller circle is $10\pi\ cm$, find the circumference of the larger circle. Also, if the area of the smaller circle is $25\pi\ cm^2$, what is the area of the larger circle?

Effortless Math Education

✎ **State if the two triangles are congruent. If they are, state how you know.**

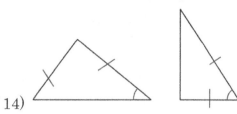

14)

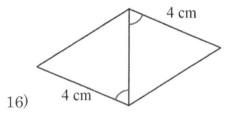

16)

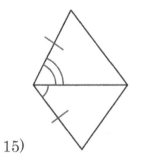

15)

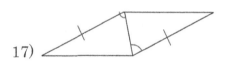

17)

✎ **State if the two triangles are congruent. If they are, state how you know.**

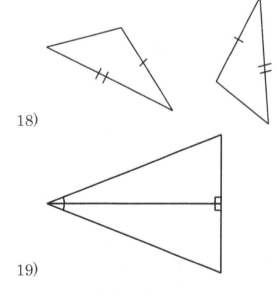

18)

19)

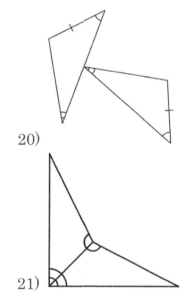

20)

21)

✎ **Solve.**

22) Are the two following triangles congruent?

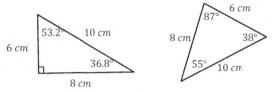

23) Are the two following Quadrilateral similar?

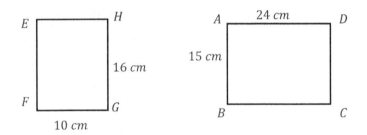

✎ **Solve.**

24) A square has a perimeter of 20 units. If the length and width are both increased by a factor of 5, what is the new perimeter and area of the square?

25) The length of a rectangular garden is 10 meters and the width is 6 meters. If the dimensions are increased by a factor of 2, what is the new perimeter, and area of the garden?

26) A cylindrical tank has a radius of 3 meters and a height of 10 meters. If these dimensions increase by a factor of 2, what will be the new surface area, and volume of the tank?

27) A circular swimming pool has a diameter of 10 meters. If the diameter increases by a factor of 2, what will be the new diameter, circumference, and area of the pool?

Effortless
Math
Education

✍ Solve.

28) A model car has a scale of $1 : 24$, which means that every inch on the model car represents 24 inches in the actual car. If the model car is 6 inches long, what is the length of the actual car in feet?

29) A map of a city block shows a width of 2 inches and a length of 3 inches. If the map is drawn with a scale factor of $\frac{1}{4}$ inch = 100 feet, what are the actual dimensions of the city block in feet?

30) A blueprint for a garden shows a rectangular plot with a length of 8 centimeters and a width of 6 centimeters. If the blueprint is a scale drawing with a scale factor of $\frac{1}{8}$ centimeter = 1 meter, what are the actual dimensions of the garden in meters?

31) A blueprint for a park shows a playground with a length of 20 meters and a width of 15 meters. If the blueprint is a scale drawing with a scale factor of $\frac{1}{5}$ meter = 1 yard, what is the actual area of the playground?

Effortless
Math
Education

✎ **Find the missing length indicated.**

32)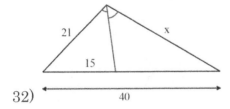

36)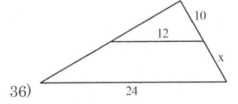

33)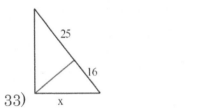

37)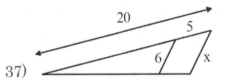

38)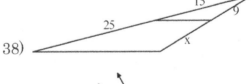

34)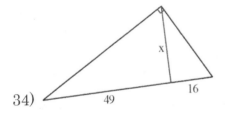

35)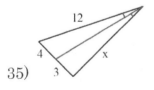

39)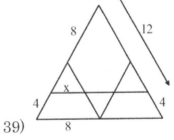

✎ **Find the scale factor of dilation of the triangle** *MNP* **to the triangle** *QRS*.

40)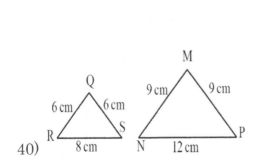

41)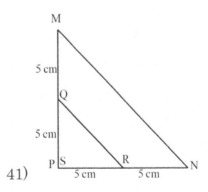

✎ **Find the scale factor of dilation of the rectangle ABCD to the rectangle EFGH.**

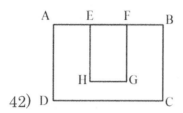

42)

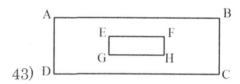

43)

✎ **Solve.**

44) A line segment has endpoints $A(-2, 4)$ and $B(6, -3)$. Find the coordinates of the point that divides AB in the ratio $2:3$.

45) A line segment has endpoints $M(3, -1)$ and $N(-5, 7)$. Find the coordinates of the point that divides MN in the ratio $3:1$.

46) A line segment has endpoints $P(1, 2)$ and $Q(7, -4)$. Find the coordinates of the point that divides PQ in the ratio $4:1$.

✎ **State if the polygons are similar.**

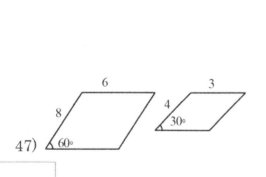

47)

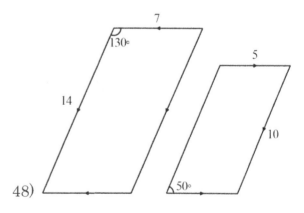

48)

✏ **The polygons in each pair are similar. Find the scale factor of the smaller figure to the larger figure.**

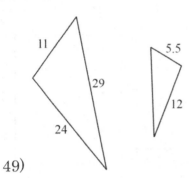

49)

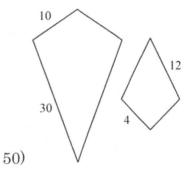

50)

✏ **Find the missing length indicated. Leave your answer in simplest radical form.**

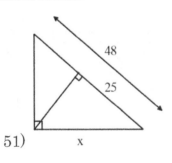

51)

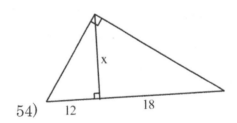

54)

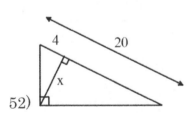

52)

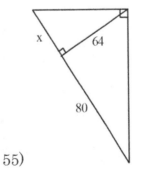

55)

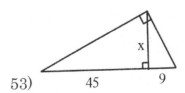

53)

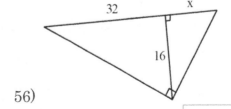

56)

Effortless
Math
Education

✎ **Solve.**

57) Two rectangular prisms are similar.
What is the volume of the larger
prisms?

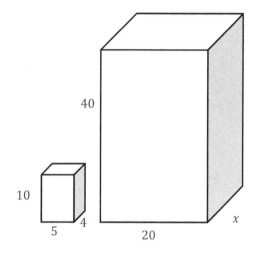

58) Two rectangular prisms are similar.
What is the volume of the smaller
prisms?

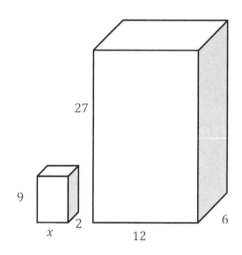

Chapter 7: Answers

1) $L = 24, W = 18$

2) $3.5, 5, 6$

3) 3

4) 7.5

5) angels unchanged, $L = 10\ cm$

6) angels unchanged

7) Similar

8) Not Similar

9) Similar

10) Similar

11) $9\ cm, 30\ cm$

12) $45\ cm, 12\ cm$

13) $16\pi, 64\pi$

14) Not congruent

15) Not congruent

16) SAS

17) SAS

18) Not congruent

19) ASA

20) AAS

21) ASA

22) Two triangles are not congruent.

23) Two quadrilaterals are similar.

24) Perimeter= 100 units, area= 625 square units

25) Perimeter= 64 meters, area= 240 square meters

26) surface area= 979.68 square meters, volume= 2260.8 cubic meters

27) circumference= 20π meters, area= 100π square meters

28) $12\ ft$

29) $800\ ft, 1,200\ ft$

30) $48\ m, 64m$

31) $7,500\ yd$

32) 35

33) 20

34) 28

35) 9

36) 10

37) 8

38) 15

39) 4

Effortless
Math
Education

40) $3:2$

41) $2:1$

42) $2:1$

43) $3:1$

44) $(\frac{6}{5}, \frac{6}{5})$

45) $(-3, 5)$

46) $(\frac{29}{5}, -\frac{14}{5})$

47) Not similar

48) Similar

49) $1:2$

50) $2:5$

51) $20\sqrt{3}$

52) 8

53) $9\sqrt{5}$

54) $6\sqrt{6}$

55) 51.2

56) 8

57) $12,800$

58) 72

CHAPTER

8 Trigonometry

Math topics that you'll learn in this chapter:

- ☑ Pythagorean Identities
- ☑ Special Right Triangles
- ☑ Trigonometric Ratios
- ☑ Trig Ratios of General Angles
- ☑ Right-Triangle Trigonometry
- ☑ Trigonometry and the Calculator
- ☑ Inverse Trigonometric Ratios
- ☑ Solving Right Triangles
- ☑ Trigonometry and Area of Triangles
- ☑ Law of Sines
- ☑ Law Cosines
- ☑ Trigonometric Applications

Pythagorean Identities

- An identity is an equation that is true for all variable values for which the variable expressions are defined.

- Since the identity $sin^2\theta + cos^2\theta = 1$ is based on the Pythagorean theorem, we refer to it as the Pythagorean identity.

- Two related Pythagorean identities can be written by dividing both sides of the equation by the same expression:

  - $1 + tan^2\theta = sec^2\theta$
  - $cot^2\theta + 1 = csc^2\theta$

Examples:

Example 1. Verify that $sin^2\frac{\pi}{4} + cos^2\frac{\pi}{4} = 1$.

Solution: $cos\frac{\pi}{4} = \frac{\sqrt{2}}{2}$ and $sin\frac{\pi}{4} = \frac{\sqrt{2}}{2}$:

$sin^2\frac{\pi}{4} + cos^2\frac{\pi}{4} = \left(\frac{\sqrt{2}}{2}\right)^2 + \left(\frac{\sqrt{2}}{2}\right)^2 = \frac{1}{2} + \frac{1}{2} = 1$

Example 2. If $cos x = \frac{3}{5}$ and x is in the 1st quadrant, find $sin x$.

Solution: Use Pythagorean identity:

$sin^2 x = 1 - cos^2 x$

$sin(x) = \pm\sqrt{1 - cos^2(x)} = \pm\sqrt{1 - \left(\frac{3}{5}\right)^2} = \pm\frac{4}{5}$

Since x is in the first quadrant, $sin x$ is positive. So $sin x = \frac{4}{5}$.

Example 3. Use a Pythagorean identity to simplify the $14 + 5\,cos^2(x) + 5\,sin^2(x)$.

Solution: The Pythagorean identity is $sin^2\theta + cos^2\theta = 1$.

$$14 + 5\,cos^2(x) + 5\,sin^2(x) = 14 + 5(cos^2(x) + sin^2(x)) = 14 + 5(1)$$

$$= 19$$

Special Right Triangles

- Special right triangles are specific right triangles with fixed angle measures and predictable side length ratios. The two main types are the $30 - 60 - 90$ and $45 - 45 - 90$ triangles.

  - $30 - 60 - 90$ triangle: Angles are $30°$, $60°$, and $90°$, with side ratios of $1 : \sqrt{3} : 2$. Trigonometric ratios are easily calculated:

    $$sin(30°) = \frac{1}{2}, \ cos(30°) = \frac{\sqrt{3}}{2}, \ tan(30°) = \frac{1}{\sqrt{3}}$$
    $$sin(60°) = \frac{\sqrt{3}}{2}, \ cos(60°) = \frac{1}{2}, \ tan(60°) = \sqrt{3}$$

  - $45 - 45 - 90$ triangle: Angles are $45°$, $45°$, and $90°$, with equal legs and a hypotenuse of leg length multiplied by $\sqrt{2}$. Trigonometric ratios are:

    $$sin(45°) = cos(45°) = \frac{1}{\sqrt{2}} \text{ or } \frac{\sqrt{2}}{2}$$
    $$tan(45°) = 1$$

- These special triangles simplify trigonometric calculations and serve as a foundation for understanding more complex problems in geometry, algebra, and calculus.

Example:

Find AC and BC in the following triangle. Round answers to the nearest tenth.

Solution: Considering that: $sin \theta = \frac{opposite}{hypotenuse}$.

Therefore: $sin 60° = \frac{AC}{15} \rightarrow 15 \times sin 60° = AC$

$$\rightarrow AC = 15 \times \frac{\sqrt{3}}{2} = 12.99 = 13.$$

According to the figure, triangle ABC is a $30 - 60 - 90$ triangle and the ratio of its sides is $1 : \sqrt{3} : 2$. Therefore, the length of side BC is half the length of AB:

$BC = \frac{1}{2} \times 15 = 7.5.$

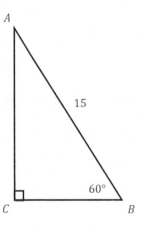

Find more at bit.ly/447bHd0

Trigonometric Ratios

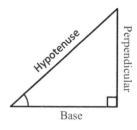

- Trigonometry is a branch of math that deals with the relationship between the angles and sides of a right-angled trigon. There are 6 trigonometric ratios: sine, cosine, tangent, secant, cosecant, and cotangent. These ratios are written as *sin*, *cos*, *tan*, *sec*, *cosec* or *csc*, and *cot* briefly. Trigonometric ratios could be accustomed to determining the ratios of any 2 sides out of a complete 3 sides of a right-angled trigon in terms of the respective angles.

- The 6 trigonometric ratios will be outlined as:

  - **sine:** The ratio of the perpendicular side of the angle to the hypotenuse.

  - **cosine:** The ratio of the side adjacent to its angle to the hypotenuse.

  - **tangent:** The ratio of the opposite side of the angle to the adjacent side of its angle.

  - **cosecant:** Cosecant could be defined as a multiplicative inverse of sine.

  - **secant:** Secant could be defined as a multiplicative inverse of cosine.

  - **cotangent:** Cotangent could be defined as the multiplicative inverse of the tangent.

Examples:

Example 1. In a right-angled trigon, right-angled at B, the hypotenuse is 12cm, the base 6cm, and the perpendicular is 4cm. If $\angle ACB = \theta$, then find the trigonometric ratio of $sin\,\theta$, and $cos\,\theta$.

Solution: We know that $sin\,\theta = \frac{perpendicular}{hypotenuse}$ and $cos\,\theta = \frac{base}{hypotenuse}$. So we put values of the hypotenuse, base, and perpendicular in these formulas to find the trigonometric ratio of $sin\,\theta$, and $cos\,\theta$: $sin\,\theta = \frac{perpendicular}{hypotenuse} \rightarrow sin\,\theta = \frac{4}{12} = \frac{1}{3} \rightarrow$ $sin\,\theta = \frac{1}{3}$. $cos\,\theta = \frac{base}{hypotenuse} \rightarrow cos\,\theta = \frac{6}{12} = \frac{1}{2} \rightarrow cos\,\theta = \frac{1}{2}$.

Example 2. Find the value of $tan\,\theta$ if $sin\,\theta = \frac{10}{3}$ and $cos\,\theta = \frac{4}{3}$.

Solution: we know that $sin\,\theta = \frac{perpendicular}{hypotenuse}$, $cos\,\theta = \frac{base}{hypotenuse}$, and $tan\,\theta = \frac{perpendicular}{base}$. According to the question, we have a trigonometric ratio of $sin\,\theta$, and $cos\,\theta$. So, we can use the numerator to find the trigonometric ratio of $tan\,\theta$: $sin\,\theta = \frac{perpendicular}{hypotenuse} = \frac{10}{3}$, and $cos\,\theta = \frac{base}{hypotenuse} = \frac{4}{3} \rightarrow tan\,\theta = \frac{perpendicular}{base} = \frac{10}{4} = \frac{5}{2}$.

Trig Ratios of General Angles

- Learn common trigonometric functions:

θ	$0°$	$30°$	$45°$	$60°$	$90°$
$sin\,\theta$	0	$\dfrac{1}{2}$	$\dfrac{\sqrt{2}}{2}$	$\dfrac{\sqrt{3}}{2}$	1
$cos\,\theta$	1	$\dfrac{\sqrt{3}}{2}$	$\dfrac{\sqrt{2}}{2}$	$\dfrac{1}{2}$	0
$tan\,\theta$	0	$\dfrac{\sqrt{3}}{3}$	1	$\sqrt{3}$	Undefined

Examples:

Find each trigonometric function.

Example 1. What is the value of $cos\,120°$?

Solution: Use the following property:

$cos(x) = sin(90° - x)$.

Therefore:

$cos\,120° = sin(90° - 120°) = sin(-30°) = -\frac{1}{2}$.

Example 2. What is the value of $sin(135°)$?

Solution: Use the following property:

$sin(x) = cos(90° - x)$.

Therefore:

$sin(135°) = cos(90° - 135°) = cos(-45°)$.

Now use the following property:

$cos(-x) = cos(x)$.

Then:

$cos(-45°) = cos(45°) = \frac{\sqrt{2}}{2}$.

bit.ly/3ZEGoET

Find more at

Right-Triangle Trigonometry

- Trigonometric ratios of an angle θ are the ratio of the lengths of the sides in a right triangle.

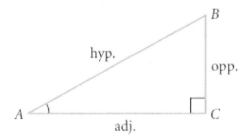

- The trigonometric functions are defined below with these abbreviations:

  ▪ $sin\,\theta = \frac{opp.}{hyp.}$

  ▪ $cos\,\theta = \frac{adj.}{hyp.}$

  ▪ $tan\,\theta = \frac{opp.}{adj.}$

  ▪ $cot\,\theta = \frac{adj.}{opp.}$

  ▪ $sec\,\theta = \frac{hyp.}{adj.}$

  ▪ $csc\,\theta = \frac{hyp.}{opp.}$

Example:

For $\Delta\,ABC$, find the side length of AB.

Solution: To find AB, use the cos ratio:

$$cos\,A = \frac{adj.}{hyp.}$$

$$cos\,41^\circ = \frac{7.1}{AB}$$

$$AB = \frac{7.1}{cos\,41^\circ}$$

$$AB = \frac{7.1}{0.75}$$

$$= 9.46$$

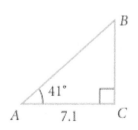

Trigonometry and the Calculator

- You can use a calculator to find the value of trigonometric functions.

- Press MODE in your calculator. The third line of that menu is DEGREE and RADIAN. These are two common measures of angles.

- These steps follow for evaluating trigonometric functions on a scientific calculator.

  - Select the correct mode (degrees or radians).

  - Click the *sin*, *cos*, or *tan* button.

  - Enter the angle measurement.

  - Click 'enter'.

Examples:

Example 1. Find $sin\ 225°$ to four decimal places.

Solution:

$sin\ 225° = -0.7071$

Example 2. Find $sec\ 44°$ to four decimal places.

Solution: $sec\ 44° = \dfrac{1}{cos\ 44°}$

$sec\ 44° = 1.3901$

Example 3. Find $cot\ 56°$.

Solution: $cot\ 56° = \dfrac{1}{tan\ 56°}$

$cot\ 56° = 0.67$

Example 4. Find $cos\ -130°$ to four decimal places.

Solution: $cos\ -130° = cos\ 130° = -0.6427$.

Inverse Trigonometric Ratios

- The inverse trigonometric ratios, often referred to as arcsine, arccosine, and arctangent (or sometimes sin^{-1}, cos^{-1}, and tan^{-1}), allow us to find the angles when given side lengths.

  - Arcsin (sin^{-1}): If $sin\,\theta = a$, then $\theta = sin^{-1}a$.

  - Arccos (cos^{-1}): If $cos\,\theta = a$, then $\theta = cos^{-1}a$.

  - Arctangent (tan^{-1}): If $tan\,\theta = a$, then $\theta = tan^{-1}a$.

- For real number inputs, the inverse trigonometric functions have specific ranges:

  - sin^{-1} returns values in the interval $-90°, 90°$ or $-\frac{\pi}{2}, \frac{\pi}{2}$ in radian.

  - cos^{-1} returns values in the interval $0°, 180°$ or $0, \pi$ in radian.

  - tan^{-1} returns values in the interval $-90°, 90°$ or $-\frac{\pi}{2}, \frac{\pi}{2}$ in radian.

- Using Inverse Trigonometric Ratios: To determine an angle in a right triangle when given the lengths of two sides:

  - Use the appropriate trigonometric ratio based on the given sides.

  - Apply the inverse trigonometric function to find the angle.

Examples:

Example 1. Given a right triangle where the length of the opposite side is 4 and the adjacent side is 3, determine the measure of the angle between the two sides.

Solution: To find the angle, use the tangent ratio.

$$tan\,\theta = \frac{4}{3}, \theta = tan^{-1}\frac{4}{3}$$

Using a calculator, θ is approximately 53.13°.

Example 2. In a right triangle, the hypotenuse is 10 cm and the side adjacent to angle α is 8 cm. What is α?

Solution: To find α, use the cosine ratio.

$$cos\,\alpha = \frac{8}{10} = 0.8, \alpha = cos^{-1}0.8$$

Using a calculator, α is approximately 36.87°.

Solving Right Triangles

- By using Sine, Cosine or Tangent, we can find an unknown side in a right triangle when we have one length, and one angle (Apart from the right angle).

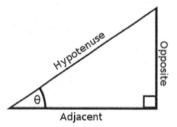

- Adjacent, Opposite and Hypotenuse, in a right triangle are shown below.

- Recall the three main trigonometric functions:

SOH–CAH–TOA, $sin\,\theta = \frac{opposite}{hypotenuse}$, $cos\,\theta = \frac{adjacent}{hypotenuse}$, $tan\,\theta = \frac{opposite}{adjacent}$.

Examples:

Example 1. Find AC in the following triangle. Round answers to the nearest tenth.

Solution: Considering that: $sin\,\theta = \frac{opposite}{hypotenuse}$.

Therefore: $sin\,45° = \frac{AC}{8} \rightarrow 8 \times sin\,45° = AC$,

Now, use a calculator to find $sin\,45°$.

$sin\,45° = \frac{\sqrt{2}}{2} \cong 0.70710$.

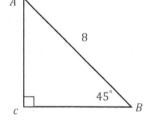

Then:

$AC = 8 \times 0.70710 = 5.6568 = 5.7$

Example 2. If $tan\,\alpha = \frac{3}{4}$, then $sin\,\alpha =?$

Solution: We know that: $tan\,\theta = \frac{opposite}{adjacent}$, and $tan\,\alpha = \frac{3}{4}$.

Therefore, the opposite side of the angle α is 3 and the adjacent side is 4. Let's draw the triangle.

Using the Pythagorean theorem, we have:

$a^2 + b^2 = c^2 \rightarrow 3^2 + 4^2 = c^2 \rightarrow 9 + 16 = c^2 \rightarrow c = 5$.

Then: $sin\,\alpha = \frac{opposite}{hypotenuse} = \frac{3}{5}$.

bit.ly/3GTpMSk

Trigonometry and Area of Triangles

- Trigonometry offers a unique method to find the area of a triangle when given two sides and the included angle. This is especially useful when the height of the triangle is not given directly or is difficult to determine.

- The area A of a triangle with sides a and b and included angle C can be found using the formula:

$$A = \frac{1}{2} \times a \times b \times \sin C$$

- This formula is derived from the height (altitude) formula. When you drop an altitude from the vertex of the angle C, it divides the base b into two parts and forms two right triangles. Using the sine function for the angle C, the height h can be expressed as $h = a \times \sin C$. Thus, the area of the triangle is, $A = \frac{1}{2} \times a \times b \times \sin C$ which leads to the above formula.

Examples:

Example 1. Find the area of a triangle with sides of lengths $5\ cm$ and $7\ cm$ and an included angle of $60°$.

Solution: Use the formula:

$$A = \frac{1}{2} \times 5 \times 7 \times \sin 60° \rightarrow A = \frac{1}{2} \times 5 \times 7 \times \frac{\sqrt{3}}{2} \rightarrow A = \frac{35\sqrt{3}}{4} \approx 15.2\ cm^2$$

Therefore, the area of this triangle is approximately $15.2\ cm^2$.

Example 2. Determine the area of a triangle where two sides are $8\ cm$ and $10\ cm$, respectively, and the angle between them measures $45°$.

Solution: Use the formula:

$$A = \frac{1}{2} \times 8 \times 10 \times \sin 45° \rightarrow A = \frac{1}{2} \times 8 \times 10 \times \frac{\sqrt{2}}{2} \rightarrow A = 20\sqrt{2} \approx 28.3\ cm^2$$

Therefore, the area of this triangle is approximately $28.3\ cm^2$.

Law of Sines

- When you know the measures of 2 factors in a triangle as well as one of the sides, as in the case of ASA or AAS, you can use the law of sines to determine the measures of the other two angles and the other side.

- For $\triangle ABC$, the Law of Sines states the following:

  ▪ $\dfrac{a}{\sin A} = \dfrac{b}{\sin B} = \dfrac{c}{\sin C}$

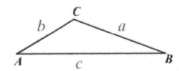

Examples:

Example 1. For a triangle, it is given $a = 12cm$, $c = 14.5cm$ and angle $C = 54°$. Find the angle A of the triangle.

Solution: Use the Law of Sines to find the side of a.

$$\frac{a}{\sin A} = \frac{c}{\sin C}$$

$$\frac{12}{\sin A} = \frac{14.5}{\sin 54°} \rightarrow \sin A = \frac{12 \times \sin 54°}{14.5}$$

$$\sin A = \frac{12 \times 0.8}{14.5} = \frac{9.6}{14.5} = 0.66 \rightarrow A = 42.3°$$

Example 2. In the ABC triangle, find side a.

Solution: Use the Law of Sines to find side a.

$$\frac{a}{\sin 30°} = \frac{54}{\sin 20°} \rightarrow a = \frac{54 \times \sin 30°}{\sin 20°}$$

$$a = \frac{54 \times 0.5}{0.34} = \frac{27}{0.34} = 79.41$$

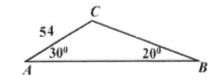

Example 3. For a triangle, it is given $A = 62°$, $B = 55°$ and $c = 5cm$. Find side b of the triangle.

Solution: Use the Law of Sines to find side b.
$62° + 55° + C = 180° \rightarrow C = 63°$

$$\frac{b}{\sin B} = \frac{c}{\sin C} \rightarrow \frac{b}{\sin 55°} = \frac{5}{\sin 63°} \rightarrow b = \frac{\sin 55° \times 5}{\sin 63°} \rightarrow b = 4.59cm$$

bit.ly/3ZEU4zq
Find more at

Law of Cosines

- The Law of Cosines can be used to find the size of the third side of a triangle when the size of the two sides and the included angle are known.

- The law of cosines can also be used to find the measure of each angle of a triangle when the measures of the three sides are known.

- The Law of Cosines states the following:

  ▪ $a^2 = b^2 + c^2 - 2bc \cos A \rightarrow \cos A = \frac{b^2 + c^2 - a^2}{2bc}$

  ▪ $b^2 = a^2 + c^2 - 2ac \cos B \rightarrow \cos B = \frac{a^2 + c^2 - b^2}{2ac}$

  ▪ $c^2 = a^2 + b^2 - 2ab \cos C \rightarrow \cos C = \frac{a^2 + b^2 - c^2}{2ab}$

Examples:

Example 1. Find angle B in the ABC triangle.

Solution: Use the Law of Cosines to find angle B.

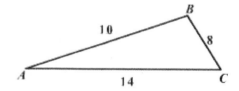

$$\cos B = \frac{a^2 + c^2 - b^2}{2ac}$$

$$\cos B = \frac{8^2 + 10^2 - 14^2}{2 \times 8 \times 10}$$

$$= \frac{64 + 100 - 196}{160} = -0.2$$

$B = 101.54°$

Example 2. For $\triangle ABC$, it is given $a = 9$, $b = 7$ and $c = 6cm$. Find angle C of the triangle.

Solution: Use the Law of Cosines to find angle C.

$$\cos C = \frac{a^2 + b^2 - c^2}{2ab} \rightarrow \cos C = \frac{9^2 + 7^2 - 6^2}{2 \times 9 \times 7} = \frac{81 + 49 - 36}{126} \cong 0.746$$

$$C = 41.75°$$

Trigonometric Applications

- The core of trigonometry is the study of relationships between the angles and sides of triangles, especially right triangles, and these principles extend to a broad range of fields such as physics, engineering, astronomy, architecture, and more.

- Physics: Trigonometry is used extensively in physics for understanding waveforms, light, and sound phenomena. For example, the sine and cosine functions describe simple harmonic motion and wave movement.

- Engineering: In engineering, trigonometry is used in calculating forces, understanding the mechanics of rotary bodies, designing bridges, buildings, and mechanical devices.

- Astronomy: Trigonometry allows astronomers to calculate distances from Earth to various celestial bodies and their relative positions in the sky.

- Architecture: Trigonometry aids in the design and planning of structures, ensuring they are both aesthetically pleasing and stable. It's used in roof inclinations, determining the height of structures, and more.

- Navigation: In navigation, trigonometry is used to find directions and distances between two locations.

Examples:

Example 1. A ladder leaning against a wall makes an angle of 60° with the ground. If the foot of the ladder is 2.5 meters from the wall, how high up the wall does the ladder reach?

Solution: The height can be found using the sine ratio: $\sin 60° = \frac{height}{ladder\ length}$

We know that: $ladder\ length = \frac{height}{\sin 60°}$

Hence: $height = 2.5\ m \times \sin 60° = 2.5 \times \frac{\sqrt{3}}{2} \approx 2.165\ m$

Example 2. A plane is flying at a height of 5,000 meters, and the pilot sees a landmark at an angle of depression of 12°. How far is the plane from the landmark along the ground (to the nearest meter)?

Solution: The distance can be found using the tangent ratio: $\tan 12° = \frac{height}{distance}$

Thus: $distance = \frac{height}{\tan 12°} = \frac{5,000\ m}{\tan 12°} = \frac{5,000}{0.21} = 23,809\ m$

(If $\tan 12° \approx 0.21$)

Chapter 8: Practices

✍ **Simplify each trigonometric expression using Pythagorean identities.**

1) $(\sin x + \cos x)^2 =$ _____

3) $\csc^2 x - \cot^2 x =$ _____

2) $(1 + \cot^2 x)\sin^2 x =$ _____

4) $2\sin^2 x + \cos^2 x =$ _____

✍ **Find the value of x and y in the following special right triangles.**

5)
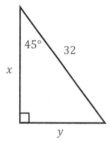

7)
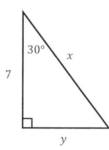

6)
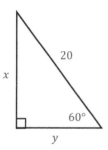

8)
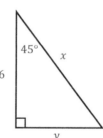

✍ **Find the given trigonometric ratio.**

9) $\tan O =$ ____

10) $\sin X =$ ____

11) $\cos X =$ ____

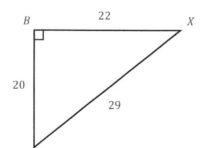

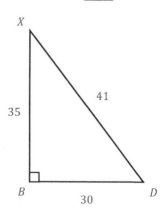

✎ **Evaluate.**

12) $sin\ 120° = $ _____

13) $sin\ -330° = $ _____

14) $tan\ -90° = $ _____

15) $cot\ 90° = $ _____

16) $cos\ -90° = $ _____

17) $sec\ 60° = $ _____

18) $csc\ 480° = $ _____

19) $cot\ -135° = $ _____

✎ **Find the measure of each side indicated. round to the nearest tent.**

20)

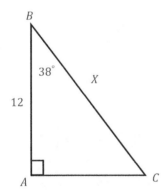

21)

22)

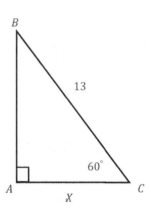

✎ **Find angles to four decimal places.**

23) $csc\ 66°$

24) $sec\ 56°$

25) $cos\ 120°$

26) $tan\ 44°$

Effortless
Math
Education

✎ **Find each angle measure to the nearest degree.**

27) $\cos A = 0.4226$

28) $\tan W = 1$

29) $\sin A = 0.9659$

30) $\tan W = 1.1106$

31) $\sin A = 0.3907$

32) $\tan W = 0.5773$

33) $\sin A = 0.5000$

34) $\cos B = 0.1392$

✎ **Find the measure of each angle indicated.**

35)

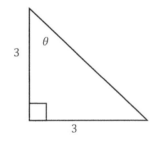

36)

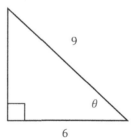

✎ **Find the missing sides. Round answers to the nearest tenth.**

37)

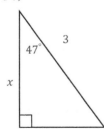

38)

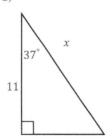

39)

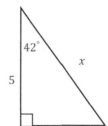

40)

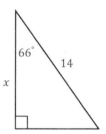

✎ **Find the area of each regular polygon. Round your answer to the nearest tenth.**

41) Perimeter = 27 mi

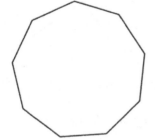

43) Perimeter = 60 cm

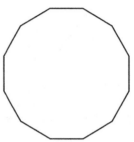

42)

8 *km*

44)

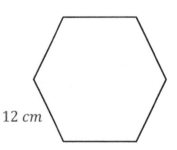

12 *cm*

45) A regular hexagon with a perimeter of 60 *yd*.

46) A regular pentagon 8 *ft* on each side.

47) A triangle with two sides that measure 15 *yd* and 26 *yd* with an included angle of 20°.

48) A triangle with two sides that measure 10 *cm* and 8 *cm* with an included angle of 77°.

Effortless
Math
Education

✎ **Find each measurement indicated. Round your answers to the nearest tenth.**

49)

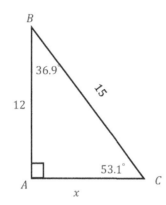

50)

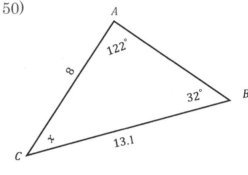

51) $m\angle C = 14°$, $m\angle A = 24°$, $c = 9$ _____

52) $m\angle C = 125°$, $b = 8$, $c = 24$ _____

✎ **Find each measurement indicated. Round your answers to the nearest tenth.**

53)

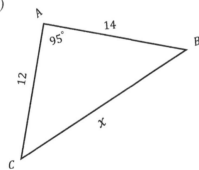

54)

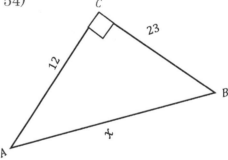

55) In $\triangle ABC$, $a = 15cm$, $b = 10cm$, $c = 7cm$ _____

56) In $\triangle ABC$, $a = 18cm$, $b = 15cm$, $c = 11cm$ _____

✎ Solve.

57) A string of a kite is 10 meters long and the inclination of the string with the ground is 30°. Find the height of the kite.

58) From the top of the tree 90 m height a man is observing the base of a tree at an angle of depression measuring 30°. Find the distance between the two trees.

59) A ladder is leaning against a vertical wall makes an angle of 45° with the ground. The foot of the ladder is 5 m from the wall. Find the length of ladder.

60) To find the height of a building, a boy measures the length of its shadow as 12 m. From the end of the shadow on the ground to the highest height of the building, He observes that an angle of 34°. Calculate the height of the building.

Effortless Math Education

Chapter 8: Answers

1) $1 + 2\sin x \cos x$

2) 1

3) 1

4) $1 + \sin^2 x$

5) $\frac{18}{19}$

6) $\frac{20}{29}$

7) $\frac{35}{41}$

8) $x = y = \frac{32}{\sqrt{2}}$ or $16\sqrt{2}$

9) $x = \frac{14\sqrt{3}}{3},\ y = \frac{7\sqrt{3}}{3}$

10) $x = 10\sqrt{3},\ y = 10$

11) $x = 6\sqrt{2},\ y = 6$

12) $\frac{\sqrt{3}}{2}$

13) $\frac{1}{2}$

14) Undefined

15) 0

16) 0

17) 2

18) $\frac{2\sqrt{3}}{3}$

19) 1

20) 15.2

21) 11.2

22) 6.5

23) 1.0946

24) 1.7882

25) -0.5

26) 0.9656

27) $65°$

28) $90°$

29) $75°$

30) $48°$

31) $23°$

32) $30°$

33) $30°$

34) $82°$

35) $45°$

36) $48.19°$

37) 2

38) 13.8

39) 6.7

40) 5.7

41) $55.6\ mi^2$

42) $27.7\ km^2$

43) $279.9\ cm^2$

44) $374.1\ cm^2$

45) $259.8\ yd^2$

46) $110.1\ ft^2$

47) $66.7\ yd^2$

48) $39.0\ cm^2$

49) $x = 9$

50) $x = 26°$

51) $m\angle B = 142°$

 $a = 15.1$

 $b = 22.9$

52) $m\angle A = 39.2°$

 $m\angle B = 15.8°$

 $a = 18.6$

53) $x = 19.2$

54) $x = 26$

55) $m\angle A = 122.9°$

 $m\angle B = 34.1°$

 $m\angle C = 23°$

56) $m\angle A = 86.1°$

 $m\angle B = 56.3°$

 $m\angle C = 37.6°$

57) $5\ m$

58) $90\sqrt{3}\ m$

59) $5\sqrt{2}\ m$

60) $8.04\ m$

Effortless Math Education

9 Circle Geometry

Math topics that you'll learn in this chapter:

- ☑ The Unit Circle
- ☑ Arc length and Sector Area
- ☑ Arcs and Central Angles
- ☑ Arcs and Chords
- ☑ Inscribed Polygons
- ☑ Inscribed Angles
- ☑ Tangents to Circles
- ☑ Secant Angles
- ☑ Secant-tangent and Tangent-tangent Angles
- ☑ Segment Lengths in Circle
- ☑ Segment Measures
- ☑ Standard Form of a Circle
- ☑ Finding the Center and the Radius of Circles
- ☑ Radian Angle Measurement

The Unit Circle

- The unit circle is a circle with a center at the origin and a radius of 1 and has the equation $x^2 + y^2 = 1$.

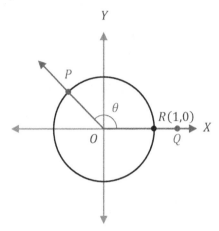

- If $\angle POQ$ is an angle in standard position and P is the point that the terminal side of the angle intersects the unit circle and $m\angle POQ = \theta$. Then:
  - The sine function is a set of ordered pairs $(\theta, \sin\theta)$ that $\sin\theta$ is the y coordinate of P.
  - The cosine function is the set of ordered pairs $(\theta, \cos\theta)$ that $\cos\theta$ is the $x-$coordinate of P.

Examples:

Example 1. If $P\left(\frac{\sqrt{3}}{2}, -\frac{1}{2}\right)$ is a point on the unit circle and the terminal side of an angle in a standard position whose size is θ. Find $\sin\theta$ and $\cos\theta$.

Solution:

$\sin\theta = y-$coordinate of $P = -\frac{1}{2}$.

$\cos\theta = x-$coordinate of $P = \frac{\sqrt{3}}{2}$.

Example 2. Does point $P\left(\frac{1}{4}, \frac{1}{4}\right)$ lie on the unit circle?

Solution: The equation of a unit circle is: $x^2 + y^2 = 1$. Now substitute $x = \frac{1}{4}$ and $y = \frac{1}{4}$:

$$\left(\frac{1}{4}\right)^2 + \left(\frac{1}{4}\right)^2 = \frac{1}{8} \neq 1$$

Since, $x^2 + y^2 \neq 1$, the point $P\left(\frac{1}{4}, \frac{1}{4}\right)$ does not lie on the unit circle.

Arc length and Sector Area

- To find a sector of a circle, use this formula:
- Area of a sector $= \pi r^2 \left(\frac{\theta}{360}\right)$.

- Where r is the radius of the circle and θ is the central angle of the sector.

- To find the arc of a sector of a circle, use this formula:
- Arc of a sector $= \left(\frac{\theta}{180}\right) \pi r$.

Examples:

Example 1. Find the length of the arc. Round your answers to the nearest

tenth. $(\pi = 3.14)$, $r = 24\ cm$, $\theta = 60°$

Solution: Use this formula: Length of a sector $= \left(\frac{\theta}{180}\right) \pi r$.

Therefore:

Length of a sector $= \left(\frac{60}{180}\right) \pi(24) = \left(\frac{1}{3}\right) \pi(24) = 8 \times 3.14 \cong 25.1\ cm$.

Example 2. Find the area of the sector. $r = 6\ ft$, $\theta = 90°$, $(\pi = 3.14)$

Solution: Use this formula: Area of a sector $= \pi r^2 \left(\frac{\theta}{360}\right)$.

Therefore:

Area of a sector $= (3.14)(6^2) \left(\frac{90}{360}\right) = (3.14)(36) \left(\frac{1}{4}\right) = 28.26\ ft^2$.

Example 3. If the length of the arc is $18,84\ cm$, where r $= 4\ cm$. Find the area of

the sector. $(\pi = 3.14)$

Solution: Use this formula: Arc of a sector $= \left(\frac{\theta}{180}\right) \pi r$.

Then:

$18.84 = (3.14)(4) \left(\frac{\theta}{180}\right) \rightarrow 18.84 = 12.56 \left(\frac{\theta}{180}\right) \rightarrow \theta = 270°$,

Now, use this formula: Area of a sector $= \pi r^2 \left(\frac{\theta}{360}\right)$.

Therefore: Area of a sector $= \left(\frac{270}{360}\right) (3.14)(4)^2 = 37.68\ cm^2$.

Arcs and Central Angles

- In the world of circle geometry, arcs and central angles are closely intertwined concepts that offer insight into the proportional relationships within a circle.

- Arcs: An arc is a segment of a circle's circumference. The size of an arc is often described in terms of its length, but it's also often represented by the measure of the central angle that it subtends.

- Central Angles: A central angle is an angle whose vertex is at the center of the circle, and its two sides (or rays) extend to the circumference, thereby subtending an arc. The measure of the central angle (in degrees or radians) is equivalent to the measure of the arc it subtends.

- Relationship Between Arcs and Central Angles (For a given circle):

  The measure of an arc (in degrees) = Measure of its central angle (in degrees)

- This relationship is because a circle contains 360°, so every portion (or arc) of the circle will be proportional to its central angle.

- The length of an arc can be determined using its central angle.

$$Arc\ Length = \left(\frac{\theta}{360}\right) 2\pi r$$

- Where: θ = Central angle in degrees, r = Radius of the circle

Example:

Find the length of the arc, for a circle with a radius of 10 units and a central angle of 120°?

Solution: To find the arc length of this circle, first use the arc length formula (Rounded to two decimal places using 3.14 for pi):

$$L = \left(\frac{120}{360}\right) 2\pi 10 \rightarrow L = \left(\frac{1}{3}\right) 62.83 \approx 20.94 \text{ units}$$

Therefore, the length of the arc is 20.94 units.

Arcs and Chords

-   The intricate relationship between arcs and chords forms a core aspect of circle geometry. Both arcs and chords reveal fascinating properties and relationships within a circle, leading to various theorems and applications.

-   **Chords:** A chord is a straight-line segment that connects two points on the circumference of a circle. The longest possible chord in a circle is the diameter.

-   Relationship Between Arcs and Chords:

    ▪   **Equal Chords and Arcs:** Chords of equal length in a circle correspond to arcs of equal lengths.
    ▪   **Perpendicular Bisector of a Chord:** The perpendicular line drawn from the center of the circle to a chord will bisect the chord, meaning it divides the chord into two equal parts.
    ▪   **Distance of Equal Arcs and Chords from Center:** Chords that create arcs of equal length are an equal distance from the center of the circle.
    ▪   **Congruent Arcs and Chords:** In the same circle or in congruent circles, two minor arcs are congruent if and only if their corresponding chords are congruent.

Examples:

Example 1. In a circle with a radius of 10 units, two chords are drawn. The first chord is 12 units long and the second chord is of unknown length. Both chords subtend arcs of equal lengths. What is the length of the second chord?

Solution: Since both chords subtend arcs of equal lengths, the lengths of the chords will be equal according to the relationship between arcs and chords. So, the second chord will also be 12 units long.

Example 2. In a circle with a radius of 10 units, a chord is drawn that is 16 units long. If a line segment is drawn from the center of the circle to the midpoint of the chord, what is the length of this line segment?

Solution: The line drawn from the center to the midpoint of the chord forms a right-angled triangle with the radius and half of the chord. Using the Pythagorean theorem (where the hypotenuse is the radius, and one side is half the length of the chord), the length of the line segment can be calculated as

follows: $length = \sqrt{radius^2 - \left(\frac{chord}{2}\right)^2} \rightarrow L = \sqrt{10^2 - \left(\frac{16}{2}\right)^2}$

$$\rightarrow L = \sqrt{100 - 64} \rightarrow L = 6 \text{ unit}$$

So, the length of the line segment is 6 units.

Inscribed Polygons

- An inscribed polygon is one that lies inside a circle such that each vertex of the polygon touches the circle. Let's dive deeper into this topic.

    - **Inscribed Triangle:** If a triangle is inscribed in a circle with one of its sides as the diameter, then it will always be a right triangle. This follows from the Inscribed Angle Theorem.

    - **Inscribed Quadrilaterals:** A quadrilateral is inscribable in a circle if and only if the sum of its opposite angles equals 180°. Such quadrilaterals are called cyclic quadrilaterals.

    $A + B = 180°$
    $C + D = 180°$

    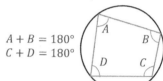

    - **Inscribed Angle and Arc:** The angle subtended by an arc at the center of the circle is double the angle subtended by it at any point on the circumference. This is known as the Inscribed Angle Theorem. For an inscribed polygon, this means the angle at a vertex of the polygon (formed by two sides touching the circle) is half of the arc's measure between those sides.

    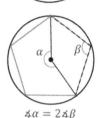

    $\sphericalangle\alpha = 2\sphericalangle\beta$

    - **Regular Polygons:** A regular polygon, a polygon with equal sides and angles, inscribed in a circle is referred to as a cyclic polygon. For a regular n-sided polygon inscribed in a circle, each central angle measures $\frac{360°}{n}$ and each inscribed angle measures $\frac{180°}{n}$.

Examples:

Example 1. A regular hexagon (a six-sided polygon) is inscribed in a circle. What is the measure of each central and inscribed angle of the hexagon?

Solution: For a regular n-sided polygon inscribed in a circle, each central angle measures $\frac{360°}{n}$ and each inscribed angle measures $\frac{180°}{n}$. For a hexagon, $n = 6$. So, each central angle $= \frac{360°}{6} = 60°$, And each inscribed angle $= \frac{180°}{6} = 30°$.

Example 2. An arc subtends an angle of 120° at the center of a circle. What is the angle subtended by the same arc at any point on the circumference of the circle?

Solution: According to the Inscribed Angle Theorem, the angle subtended by an arc at a point on the circumference is half the angle it subtends at the center. Therefore, the angle subtended on the circumference is $\frac{120°}{2} = 60°$.

Inscribed Angles

- An inscribed angle is formed when two chords in a circle intersect or come together at a single point on the circle's circumference.

- Key Properties of Inscribed Angles:

  - **Inscribed Angle and its Intercepted Arc:** The measure of an inscribed angle is half the measure of its intercepted arc. This is often called the Inscribed Angle Theorem.

    $$\sphericalangle ABC = \frac{1}{2}\widehat{AC}$$

    Where $\sphericalangle ABC$ is the measure of the inscribed angle, and Arc AC is the measure of the intercepted arc.

    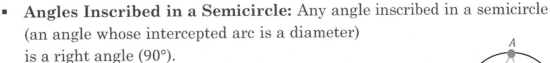

  - **Angles Inscribed in a Semicircle:** Any angle inscribed in a semicircle (an angle whose intercepted arc is a diameter) is a right angle (90°).

  - **Angles Inscribed in the Same Arc:** If two inscribed angles intercept the same arc (or, equivalently, if their chords are subtended by the same arc), they are congruent.

    $\angle ABC = \angle ADC$
    $\angle BAD = \angle BCD$

    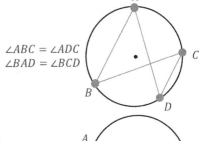

  - **Angle Formed by a Tangent and a Chord:** When a tangent at a point on a circle intersects a chord, the angle formed is half the measure of the arc intercepted by that chord.

    $\alpha = \frac{1}{2}\widehat{AB}$

    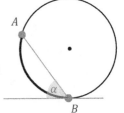

Example:

In a semicircle with diameter AB of length $16\ cm$, a point C is chosen on the circumference to inscribe an angle ACB. If $AC = 10\ cm$, find the length of BC.

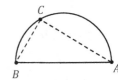

Solution: Since angle ACB is inscribed in the semicircle, it forms a right angle. Therefore, triangle ACB is a right triangle, and we can use the Pythagorean theorem to find BC: $BC = \sqrt{AB^2 - AC^2}$

$\rightarrow BC = \sqrt{16^2 - 10^2} \rightarrow BC = \sqrt{156} \rightarrow BC = 2\sqrt{39} \approx 12.49\ cm$

So, the length of BC is $2\sqrt{39}\ cm$ or approximately $12.49\ cm$.

bit.ly/3u4Ojja

Find more at

Tangents to Circles

- A tangent to a circle is a straight line that touches the circle at exactly one point without crossing it. This singular point of contact is termed the "point of tangency."

- Key Properties and Theorems Related to Tangents:

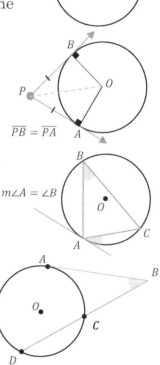

- **Tangent-Radius Perpendicularity:** The radius drawn to the point of tangency is always perpendicular to the tangent at that point.

- **Length of Two Tangent Segments from a Point:** From an external point, if two tangents are drawn to a circle, the lengths of these tangent segments (from the external point to the point of tangency) are equal. $\overline{PB} = \overline{PA}$

- **Angle between Tangent and Chord:** The angle formed between a tangent and a chord is equal to half the measure of the arc intercepted by that chord. $m\angle A = \angle B$

- **Angles Formed by Tangent-Secant Lines**: When a tangent and a secant line emanate from the same external point, the measure of the angle formed between them is half the difference between the larger intercepted arc and the smaller intercepted arc.

Example:

A circle has a radius of $7\ cm$ and a tangent is drawn from a point $24\ cm$ away from the center of the circle. What is the length of the tangent?

Solution: The tangent drawn from an external point to a circle forms a right angle with the radius at the point of contact. Thus, in this case, we have a right triangle formed by the radius, the distance from the center to the external point, and the tangent. Using the Pythagorean theorem, the length of the tangent AB is given by:

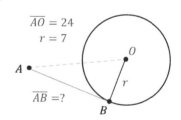

$$\overline{AB} = \sqrt{24^2 - 7^2} = \sqrt{576 - 49} = \sqrt{527} \approx 23\ cm$$

Secant Angles

- A secant is a straight line that intersects a circle at two distinct points. When two secants emanate from an external point and intersect the circle, the angle they form outside the circle is termed a secant-secant angle.

- Key Properties and Theorems Related to Secant Angles:

  ▪ **Secant-Secant Angle:** When two secants are drawn from an external point and intersect the circle at points A, B and C, D respectively, the measure of the angle formed by these secants is half the difference of the measures of the intercepted arcs.

  $$m\angle BCD = \frac{\widehat{AE} - \widehat{BD}}{2}$$

  ▪ **Secant-Tangent Angle:** When a secant and a tangent emanate from the same external point and intersect the circle, the measure of the angle they form is half the difference between the intercepted arc (by the secant) and the arc subtended by the chord (from the point of tangency to the secant's other intersection point).

  $$m\angle BCD = \frac{1}{2}\widehat{BA} \quad \text{or} \quad m\angle BCD = \frac{\widehat{AD} - \widehat{BD}}{2}$$

Example:

Two secant lines ABC and ADE intersect outside a circle at point A. Arc CE measures $140°$ and Arc BD measures $80°$. What is the measure of $\angle A$?

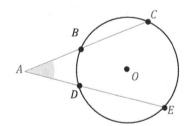

Solution: According to the formula for the angles between two secants intersecting outside a circle, the measure of $\angle A$ is half the difference of the measures of the intercepted arcs, i.e.,

$$m\angle A = \left(\tfrac{1}{2}\right) \times \left(\widehat{CE} - \widehat{BD}\right) = \left(\tfrac{1}{2}\right) \times (140° - 80°) = 30°$$

So, $\angle A$ measures $30°$.

bit.ly/46SRjxV

Secant-tangent and Tangent-tangent Angles

- While we have discussed secant-secant angles, two other important angle types involve the combination of secants and tangents:

  - **Secant-Tangent Angle:** When a secant and a tangent emanate from the same external point and intersect the circle, the measure of the angle they form is half the measure of the intercepted arc by the secant.

  $$m\angle BCD = \frac{1}{2}\overset{\frown}{BA} \text{ or } m\angle BCD = \frac{\overset{\frown}{AD}-\overset{\frown}{BD}}{2}$$

  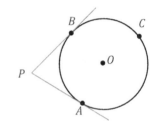

  - **Tangent-Tangent Angle:** When two tangents are drawn from an external point and touch the circle, the measure of the angle they form is half the difference of the measures of the intercepted arcs.

  $$m\angle P = \frac{\overset{\frown}{BCA}-\overset{\frown}{BA}}{2}$$

  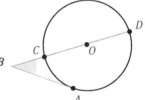

Examples:

Example 1. $\overline{DC}$ is a diameter. The ratio of Arc AD to arc AC is $5:1$. what is $m\angle ABC$?

Solution: In the circle where $\overline{DC}$ is a diameter, if the ratio of $\overset{\frown}{AD}$ to $\overset{\frown}{AC}$ is $5:1$, this means that the Semicircle is divided into 6 equal parts and $\overset{\frown}{AD}$ comprises 5 parts of it while $\overset{\frown}{AC}$ comprises 1 part of it. Since the total measure of a Semicircle is 180 degrees, each part is $\frac{180°}{6} = 30°$.
The measure of $\angle ABC$ is calculated by the formula:
$m\angle ABC = \frac{m\angle AD - m\angle AC}{2} = \frac{(5\times30)-(1\times30)}{2} = \frac{120}{2} = 60$
Therefore, the measure of $\angle ABC$ is $60°$.

Example 2. Two tangents, PQ and PR, are drawn from an external point P to a circle. If arc QR measures $120°$, what is the measure of $\angle QPR$?

Solution: The measure of the angle between two tangents drawn from an external point to a circle is half the measure of the intercepted arc. Therefore:
$m\angle QPR = \frac{(360-120)-120}{2} = \frac{120}{2} = 60°$

So, the measure of angle QPR is $60°$.

Segment Lengths in Circle

In a circle, there are various segments formed by chords, tangents, and secants. Some important theorems related to these segments are:

- **Chord-Chord Power Theorem:** When two chords intersect inside a circle.
  If a chord AB intersects chord CD at point E inside the circle, then: $AE \times EB = CE \times ED$

- **Tangent-Secant Power Theorem:** When an external point touches a circle creating a tangent and also extends to cut the circle (forming a secant).

  If a tangent from an external point A touches the circle at point B and the secant from A cuts the circle at points C and D (with D being the farther point), then: $AB^2 = AC \times AD$

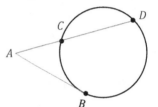

- **Secant-Secant Power Theorem:** When two secants intersect at an external point and cut the circle.

  If secant AE and secant BD intersect at point C outside the circle and cut the circle at points A, E, B, and D respectively, then: $AC \times CE = BC \times CD$

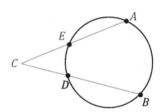

Example:

Consider the figure below, then find the length of EF?

Solution: To solve this problem, we'll make use of the Tangent-Secant Power Theorem and the Chord-Chord Power Theorem.

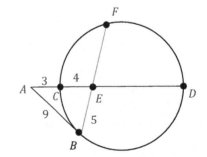

Using the Tangent-Secant Power Theorem (Since $AD = AC + CD$):

$AB^2 = AC \times (AC + CD) \rightarrow 9^2 = 3 \times (3 + CD) \rightarrow 3CD = \frac{81-9}{3} \rightarrow CD = 24$

Now, using the Chord-Chord Power Theorem on the chords BF and CD (Since $CD = CE + ED \rightarrow ED = 24 - 4 \rightarrow ED = 40$):

$$BE \times EF = CE \times ED \rightarrow 5 \times EF = 4 \times 20 \rightarrow EF = \frac{80}{5} \rightarrow EF = 16$$

Therefore, the length of EF is 16 units.

bit.ly/46SRn0D

Find more at

Segment Measures

- A segment in a circle refers to the region between a chord and the arc subtended by that chord. Essentially, it's a piece of the circle "cut off" by a chord. Depending on the context, when talking about "segment measures," we could be referring to the length of the chord, the length of the arc, or the area of the segment.

- Types of Segments:
    - **Minor Segment:** The smaller area between a chord and its corresponding arc.
    - **Major Segment:** The larger area between a chord and its arc.

- Key Properties and Formulas:
    - **Arc Length:** Arc length L can be found using the formula: $L = \left(\frac{\theta}{360}\right) 2\pi r$
      Where θ is the central angle in degrees and r is the radius.
    - **Area of a Segment:** $Area = \left(\frac{1}{2}\right) \times r^2 \times \left(\theta\left(\frac{\pi}{180}\right) - \sin\theta\right)$
      Here, θ is the central angle in radians.

Examples:

Example 1. If the radius of a circle is kept constant at $10\ cm$, How much would the arc length change if the central angle is doubled from $60°$ to $120°$?

Solution: If the central angle is doubled, the arc length will also double. This is because the arc length is directly proportional to the central angle in a circle with a constant radius. So, if the arc length for a $60°$ central angle was calculated as approximately $L = \left(\frac{60}{360}\right) 2\pi r = 10.47\ cm$, the arc length for a $120°$ central angle would be approximately $2 \times 10.47\ cm = 20.94\ cm$.

Example 2. What is the area of a segment in a circle with a radius of $10\ cm$ that subtends a central angle of $30°$?

Solution: The area of a segment can be calculated by subtracting the area of the triangle formed by the radius and the subtended angle from the area of the sector. The area of the sector is given by the formula $\left(\frac{\theta}{360}\right)\pi r^2 = \frac{1}{12}\pi 100 = \frac{25}{3}\pi$, and the area of the triangle is given by $\frac{1}{2} \times r^2 \sin\theta = 25$. So, the area of the segment $=$ area of the sector $-$ area of the triangle $= \frac{25}{3}\pi - 25 =\approx 1.17\ cm^2$.

Standard Form of a Circle

- Equation of circles in standard form: $(x - h)^2 + (y - k)^2 = r^2$.

- Center: (h, k), Radius: r.

- General format: $ax^2 + by^2 + cx + dy + e = 0$.

Examples:

Write the standard form equation of each circle.

Example 1. Center: $(-9, -12)$, Radius: 4.

Solution: $(x - h)^2 + (y - k)^2 = r^2$ is the circle equation with a radius r, centered at (h, k). We have:

$h = -9$, $k = -12$ and $r = 4$.

Then:

$$\left(x - (-9)\right)^2 + \left(y - (-12)\right)^2 = (4)^2 \rightarrow (x + 9)^2 + (y + 12)^2 = 16.$$

Example 2. $x^2 + y^2 - 8x - 6y + 21 = 0$.

Solution: $(x - h)^2 + (y - k)^2 = r^2$ is the circle equation with a radius r, centered at (h, k). First move the loose number to the right side:

$x^2 + y^2 - 8x - 6y = -21$.

Group x −variables and y −variables together:

$(x^2 - 8x) + (y^2 - 6y) = -21$.

Convert x to square form:

$(x^2 - 8x + 16) + (y^2 - 6y) = -21 + 16 \rightarrow (x - 4)^2 + (y^2 - 6y) = -5$.

Convert y to square form:

$(x - 4)^2 + (y^2 - 6y + 9) = -21 + 16 + 9 \rightarrow (x - 4)^2 + (y - 3)^2 = 4$.

Then:

$$(x - 4)^2 + (y - 3)^2 = 2^2$$

bit.ly/3CG6a1A

Find more at

Finding the Center and the Radius of Circles

- $(x-h)^2 + (y-k)^2 = r^2$

Center: (h, k), Radius: r.

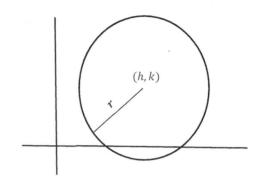

Examples:

Identify the center and radius.

Example 1. $x^2 + y^2 - 4y + 3 = 0$.

Solution: $(x-h)^2 + (y-k)^2 = r^2$ is the circle equation with a radius r, centered at (h, k). Rewrite $x^2 + y^2 - 4y + 3 = 0$ in the form of the standard circle equation:

Group x −variables and y −variables together:

$(x^2) + (y^2 - 4y) = -3$.

Convert x and y to square form:

$(x^2) + (y^2 - 4y + 4) - 4 = -3$.

Therefore:

$(x - 0)^2 + (y - 2)^2 = 1^2$.

Then:

Center: $(0,2)$ and $r = 1$.

Example 2. $4x + x^2 - 6y = 24 - y^2$.

Solution: $(x-h)^2 + (y-k)^2 = r^2$ is the circle equation with a radius r, centered at (h, k). Rewrite $4x + x^2 - 6y = 24 - y^2$ in the form of the standard circle equation:

$$\left(x - (-2)\right)^2 + (y - 3)^2 = \left(\sqrt{37}\right)^2.$$

Then: Center: $(-2,3)$ and $r = \sqrt{37}$.

Radian Angle Measure

- To convert degrees to radians, use this formula: $Radian = Degrees \times \frac{\pi}{180}$.

- To convert radians to degrees, use this formula: $Degrees = Radian \times \frac{180}{\pi}$.

Examples:

Example 1. Convert 120 degrees to radians.

Solution: Use this formula:

$Radian = Degrees \times \frac{\pi}{180}$.

Therefore:

$Radian = 120 \times \frac{\pi}{180} = \frac{120\pi}{180} = \frac{2\pi}{3}$.

Example 2. Convert $\frac{\pi}{3}$ to degrees.

Solution: Use this formula:

$Degrees = Radians \times \frac{180}{\pi}$.

Then:

$Degrees = \frac{\pi}{3} \times \frac{180}{\pi} = \frac{180\pi}{3\pi} = 60$.

Example 3. Convert $\frac{2\pi}{5}$ to degrees.

Solution: Use this formula:

$Degrees = Radians \times \frac{180}{\pi}$.

Therefore:

$Degrees = \frac{2\pi}{5} \times \frac{180}{\pi} = \frac{360\pi}{5\pi} = 72$.

Example 4. Convert 45 degrees to radians.

Solution: Use this formula:

$Radian = Degrees \times \frac{\pi}{180}$.

Therefore:

$Radian = 45 \times \frac{\pi}{180} = \frac{45\pi}{180} = \frac{\pi}{4}$.

bit.ly/3pxMlAh

Find more at

Chapter 9: Practices

✎ **Solve.**

1) If $P(-\frac{\sqrt{3}}{2}, \frac{1}{2})$ is a point on the unit circle and the terminal side of an

   angle in a standard position whose size is θ. Find $sin\,\theta$ and $cos\,\theta$.

   _____

2) If $P(\frac{\sqrt{2}}{2}, -\frac{\sqrt{2}}{2})$ is a point on the unit circle and the terminal side of an

   angle in a standard position whose size is θ. Find $sin\,\theta$ and $cos\,\theta$.

   _____

✎ **Find the length of each arc. Round your answers to the nearest tenth.**

3) $r = 14ft, \theta = 45°$

4) $r = 18m, \theta = 60°$

5) $r = 26m, \theta = 90°$

6) $r = 20m, \theta = 120°$

✎ **Find the area of the sector. Round your answers to the nearest tenth.**

7) $r = 4m, \theta = 20°$

8) $r = 2m, \theta = 45°$

9) $r = 8m, \theta = 90°$

10) $r = 4m, \theta = 135°$

✍ **Name the central angle of the given arc.**

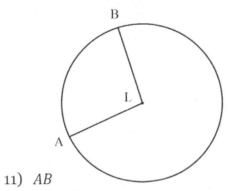

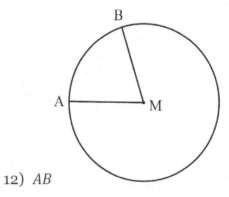

11) AB 12) AB

✍ **Solve for x. Assume that lines which appear to be diameters are actual diameters.**

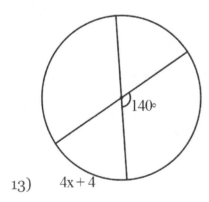

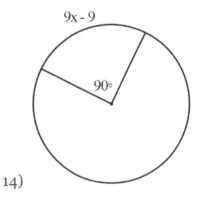

13)   14)

✍ **Find the measure of the arc or central angle indicated. Assume that lines which appear to be diameters are actual diameters.**

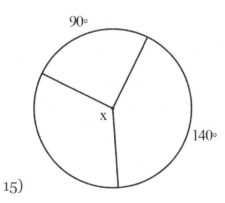

15)

Effortless
Math
Education

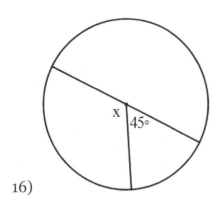

16)

🖎 **Find the length of the segment indicated. Round your answer to the nearest tenth if necessary.**

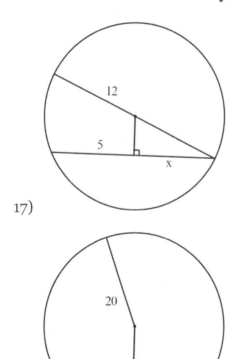

17)

18)

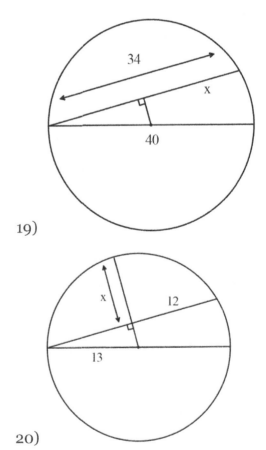

19)

20)

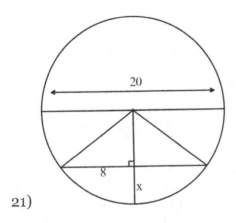

21)

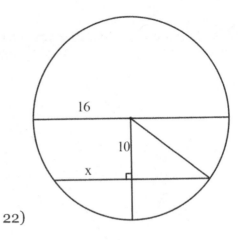

22)

🖎 **State if each polygon is an inscribed polygon.**

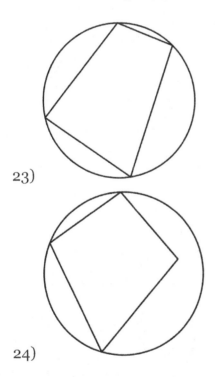

23)

25)

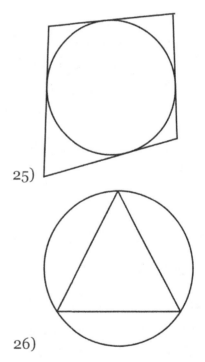

24)

26)

✎ **Find the value of each variable.**

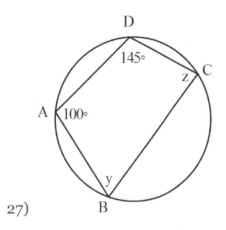

27)

28)

✎ **State if each angle is an inscribed angle. If it is, name the angle and the intercepted arc.**

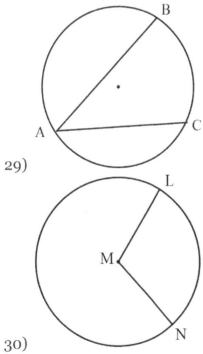

29)

31)

30)

32)

✎ **Find the measure of the angle ∠BAC.**

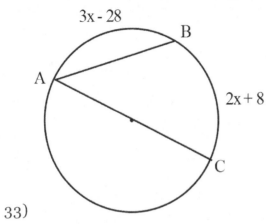

33)

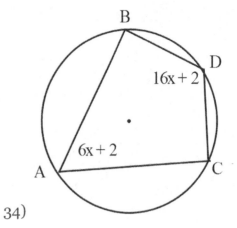

34)

✎ **Find the segment length indicated. Assume that lines which appear to be tangent are tangent.**

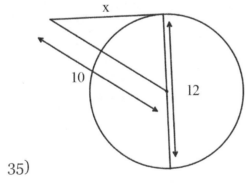

35)

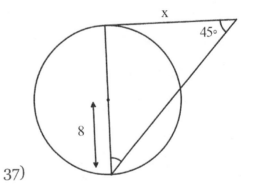

37)

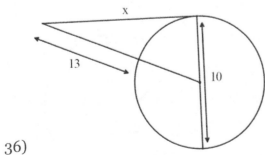

36)

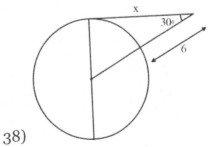

38)

Effortless

Math

Education

✎ **Find the perimeter of each polygon. Assume that lines which appear to be tangent are tangent.**

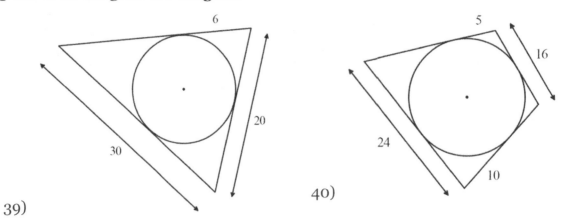

39)

40)

✎ **Find the measure of the arc or angle indicated. Assume that lines which appear tangent are tangent.**

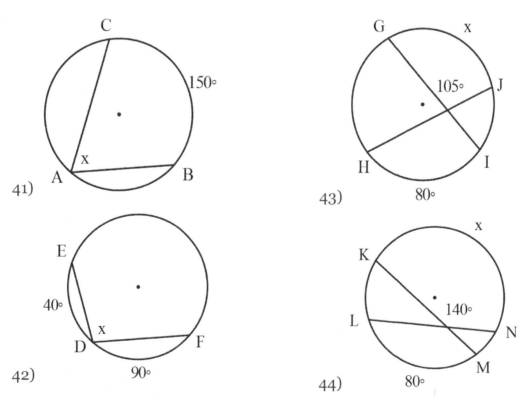

41)

42)

43)

44)

✑ **Solve for *x*. assume that lines which appear tangent are tangent.**

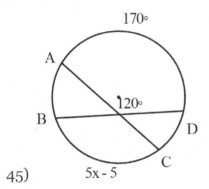

45)

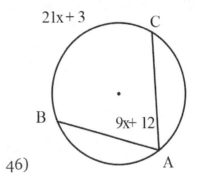

46)

✑ **Solve for *x*. assume that lines which appear tangent are tangent.**

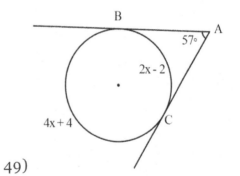

47)

49)

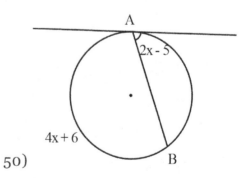

48)

50)

✎ **Find the measure of the arc or angle indicated. Assume that lines which appear tangent are tangent.**

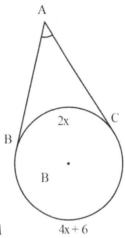

51) Find $m\angle A$

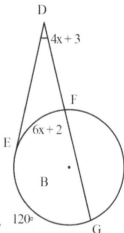

52) Find arc EF

✎ **Find the measure of the line segment indicated. Assume that lines which appear tangent are tangent.**

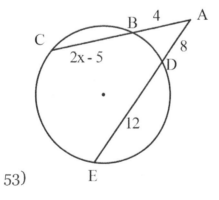

53)

54)

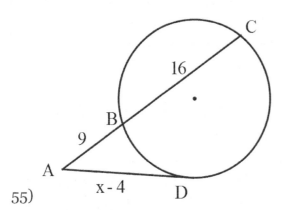

55)

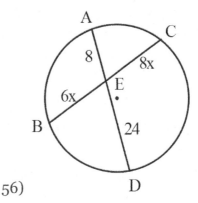

56)

✎ **Solve for x. Assume that lines which appear tangent are tangent.**

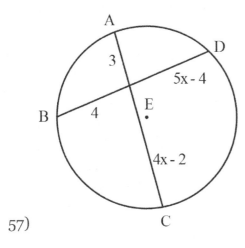

57)

✎ **Write the standard form equation of each circle.**

58) $y^2 + 2x + x^2 = 24y - 120$

59) $x^2 + y^2 - 2y - 15 = 0$

60) $8x + x^2 - 2y = 64 - y^2$

61) Center: $(-5, -6)$, Radius: 9

62) Center: $(-12, -5)$, Area: 4π

63) Center: $(-11, -14)$, Area: 16π

Effortless
Math
Education

64) Center: $(-3,2)$, Circumference: 2π

65) Center: $(15,14)$, Circumference: $2\pi\sqrt{15}$

✒ Identify the center and radius of each.

66) $(x-2)^2 + (y+5)^2 = 10$ 68) $(x-2)^2 + (y+6)^2 = 9$

67) $x^2 + (y-1)^2 = 4$ 69) $(x+14)^2 + (y-5)^2 = 16$

✒ Convert each degree measure into radians.

70) $-150^\circ = $ _____   73) $-60^\circ = $ _____

71) $420^\circ = $ _____   74) $315^\circ = $ _____

72) $300^\circ = $ _____   75) $600^\circ = $ _____

✒ Convert each radian measure into degrees.

76) $-\frac{16\pi}{3} = $ 79) $\frac{5\pi}{9} = $

77) $-\frac{3\pi}{5} = $ 80) $-\frac{\pi}{3} = $

78) $\frac{11\pi}{6} = $ 81) $\frac{13\pi}{6} = $

Effortless
Math
Education

Chapter 9: Answers

1) $sin\,\theta = y$ −coordinate of $P = \frac{1}{2}$

   $cos\,\theta = x$ −coordinate of $P = -\frac{\sqrt{3}}{2}$

2) $sin\,\theta = y$ −coordinate of $P = -\frac{\sqrt{2}}{2}$

   $cos\,\theta = x$ −coordinate of $P = \frac{\sqrt{2}}{2}$

3) 11.0

4) 18.8

5) 40.8

6) 41.9

7) 2.8

8) 1.6

9) 50.3

10) 18.8

11) $\angle L$

12) $\angle AMB$

13) 9

14) 11

15) 130°

16) 135°

17) 5

18) 16

19) 17

20) 8

21) 4

22) 12.5

23) Yes

24) No

25) No

26) Yes

27) $y = 35°$, $z = 80°$

28) $\angle E = \angle C \;\rightarrow (3x - 10) + 2 \times (2x + 10) = 360° \;\rightarrow x = 50$

   $\angle E = \angle C = 110°$, $\angle D = 140°$

29) Yes; $m\angle BAC, \overset{\frown}{BC}$

30) NO

31) Yes; $m\angle YXZ, \overset{\frown}{YZ}$

32) NO

33) $m\angle BAC = 44°$

34) $m\angle BAC = 50°$

35) 8

36) 17.3

37) 16

38) 10.4

39) 72

40) 80

41) 75°

42) 115°

43) 130°

44) 200°

45) 15

46) 7

47) 45

48) 27

49) 54

50) 23

51) 62°

52) 50°

53) 20.5

54) 11

55) 15

56) 16

57) 1.25

58) $(x + 1)^2 + (y - 12)^2 = 25$

59) $x^2 + (y - 1)^2 = 16$

60) $(x + 4)^2 + (y - 1)^2 = 81$

61) $(x + 5)^2 + (y + 6)^2 = 81$

62) $(x + 12)^2 + (y + 5)^2 = 4$

63) $(x + 11)^2 + (y + 14)^2 = 16$

64) $(x + 3)^2 + (y - 2)^2 = 1$

65) $(x - 15)^2 + (y - 14)^2 = 15$

66) Center: $(2, -5)$, Radius: $\sqrt{10}$

67) Center: $(0, 1)$, Radius: 2

68) Center: $(2, -6)$, Radius: 3

69) Center: $(-14, 5)$, Radius: 4

70) $-\frac{5\pi}{6}$

71) $\frac{7\pi}{3}$

72) $\frac{5\pi}{3}$

73) $-\frac{\pi}{3}$

74) $\frac{7\pi}{4}$

75) $\frac{10\pi}{3}$

76) $-960°$

77) $-108°$

78) $330°$

79) $100°$

80) $-60°$

81) $390°$

10 Surface Area and Volume

Math topics that you'll learn in this chapter:

- ☑ Circumference and Area of a Circle
- ☑ Area of a Trapezoids
- ☑ Area of Polygons
- ☑ Nets of 3-D Figures
- ☑ Cubes
- ☑ Rectangular Prisms
- ☑ Cylinder
- ☑ Surface Area of Prisms and Cylinders
- ☑ Volume of Cones and Pyramids
- ☑ Surface Area of Pyramids and Cones
- ☑ Volume of Spheres
- ☑ Sphere Surface Area
- ☑ Solids and Their Cross Sections
- ☑ Volume of a Truncated Cone

Circumference and Area of a Circles

- In a circle, variable r is usually used for the radius and d for diameter.

$$Area\ of\ a\ circle = \pi r^2\ (\pi\ is\ about\ 3.14)$$

$$Circumference\ of\ a\ circle = 2\pi r$$

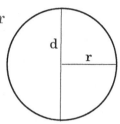

Examples:

Example 1. Find the Circumference of this circle. ($\pi = 3.14$)

Solution: Use Circumference formula: $Circumference = 2\pi r$

$r = 8\ cm \rightarrow Circumference = 2\pi(8) = 16\pi$

$\pi = 3.14$, Then: $Circumference = 16 \times 3.14 = 50.24\ cm$

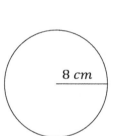

Example 2. Find the area of this circle.

Solution: Use area formula: $Area = \pi r^2$

$r = 9\ in$, Then: $Area = \pi(9)^2 = 81\pi$, $\pi = 3.14$

$$Area = 81 \times 3.14 = 254.34\ in^2$$

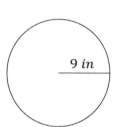

Example 3. Find the Circumference of this circle.($\pi = 3.14$)

Solution: Use Circumference formula:

$$Circumference = 2\pi r$$

$r = 10\ m \rightarrow Circumference = 2\pi(10) = 20\pi$

$\pi = 3.14$, Then: $Circumference = 20 \times 3.14 = 60.8\ m$

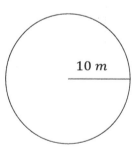

Example 4. Find the area of this circle. ($\pi = 3.14$)

Solution: Use area formula: $Area = \pi r^2$

$r = 6\ in \rightarrow Area = \pi(6)^2 = 36\pi$, $\pi = 3.14$

Then: $Area = 36 \times 3.14 = 113.04\ in^2$

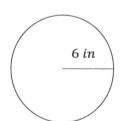

Area of a Trapezoids

- A quadrilateral with at least one pair of parallel sides is a trapezoid.

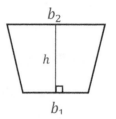

- Area of a trapezoid $= \frac{1}{2}h(b_1 + b_2)$

Examples:

Example 1. Calculate the area of this trapezoid.

Solution:

Use area formula: $A = \frac{1}{2}h(b_1 + b_2)$

$b_1 = 6\ cm$, $b_2 = 10\ cm$ and $h = 12\ cm$

Then: $A = \frac{1}{2}(12)(10 + 6) = 6(16) = 96\ cm^2$

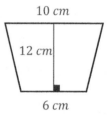

Example 2. Calculate the area of this trapezoid.

Solution:

Use area formula: $A = \frac{1}{2}h(b_1 + b_2)$

$b_1 = 10\ cm$, $b_2 = 18\ cm$ and $h = 14\ cm$

Then: $A = \frac{1}{2}(14)(10 + 18) = 196\ cm^2$

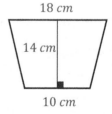

Example 3. Calculate the area of this trapezoid.

Solution:

Use area formula: $A = \frac{1}{2}h(b_1 + b_2)$

$b_1 = 21\ cm$, $b_2 = 15\ cm$ and $h = 16\ cm$

Then: $A = \frac{1}{2}(16)(21 + 15) = 288\ cm^2$

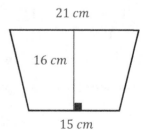

Area of Polygons

- Polygons are flat, closed shapes defined by straight lines. The study of their areas is an essential topic in geometry as it provides a deeper understanding of space utilization and measurement.

- **Triangle:** $Area = \frac{1}{2} \times base \times height$

- **Rectangle:** $Area = length \times width$

- **Square:** $Area = side^2$

- **Parallelogram:** $Area = base \times height$

- **Trapezoid:** $Area = \frac{1}{2}(base1 + base2) \times height$

- **Regular Polygon:** A polygon with all sides and angles equal.

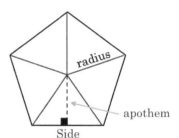

$$Area = \frac{1}{2} perimeter \times apothem$$

Where apothem is the perpendicular distance from the center to a side.

Example:

A jewel is cut in the shape of a regular octagon. Each side of the octagon measures $4\ mm$. What is the area of the jewel's face?

Solution: First, find the apothem. In a regular octagon, each angle at the center is $\frac{360°}{8} = 45°$, which forms a right triangle with a $22.5°$ angle. Therefore, the apothem is:

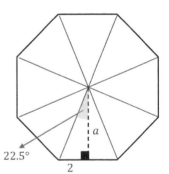

$$\tan 22.5° = \frac{2}{a} \rightarrow a = \frac{2}{\tan 22.5°} = 2(\sqrt{2} + 1)\ mm$$

Then, find the perimeter: $8 \times 4 = 32\ mm$

Finally, find the area.

Use the formula for the area of a regular polygon, $A = \frac{1}{2} \times p \times a$.

Substitute $2(\sqrt{2} + 1)\ mm$ for a and $32mm$ for p:

$$A = \frac{1}{2} \times 32 \times 2(\sqrt{2} + 1) = 32(\sqrt{2} + 1) \approx 77.25\ mm^2$$

So, the area of the jewel's face is about $77.25\ mm^2$.

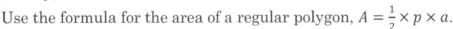

Nets of 3-D Figures

- A three-dimensional figure's net is a two-dimensional representation of that figure. It is analogous to how a wireframe is a two-dimensional representation of a three-dimensional object. Nets can help us understand the properties of 3-*D* figures, as they can be used to visualize the figure in question. For instance, a cube's net is not simply a square, but rather a series of squares connected in a specific arrangement. This means that if you were to take a piece of paper and have it fold it into a specific square shape, you would have created the cube's net. However, there are many other potential nets for a cube and other three-dimensional figures. In fact, there are numerous, but not infinitely many, possible nets for any given three-dimensional figure. Understanding how to create and interpret nets can be helpful in understanding the more complex properties of 3-*D* figures, such as surface area and volume.

Examples:

Example 1. Create a net for the following figure.
Solution: To create a net for a shape, you must first understand what geometric shapes the shape is made of. This prism is made up of two pentagons and five rectangles.

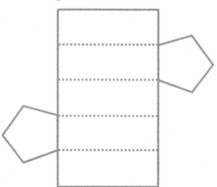

Example 2. A rectangular prism has a length of 3 *cm*, a width of 2 *cm*, and a height of 10 *cm*. Create a net for the rectangular prism.
Solution: To create a net for the rectangular prism, you can imagine unfolding the sides of the prism to create a flat, two-dimensional shape. The net for this rectangular prism would consist of six rectangles, with two of them having a length of 10 *cm* and a width of 3 cm, two of them having a length of 10 *cm* and a width of 2 *cm*, and two of them having a length of 3 *cm* and a width of 2 *cm*.

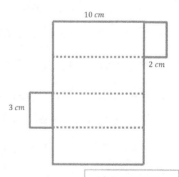

bit.ly/3rgAz3n

Find more at

Cubes

- A cube is a three-dimensional solid object bounded by six square sides.

- Volume is the measure of the amount of space inside of a solid figure, like a cube, ball, cylinder or pyramid.

- The volume of a cube = $(one\ side)^3$

- The surface area of a cube = $6 \times (one\ side)^2$

Examples:

Example 1. Find the volume and surface area of this cube.

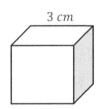

Solution: Use volume formula: $volume = (one\ side)^3$
Then: $volume = (one\ side)^3 = (3)^3 = 27\ cm^3$
Use surface area formula:
$surface\ area\ of\ a\ cube$: $6(one\ side)^2 = 6(3)^2 = 6(9) = 54\ cm^2$

Example 2. Find the volume and surface area of this cube.

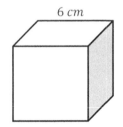

Solution: Use volume formula: $volume = (one\ side)^3$
Then: $volume = (one\ side)^3 = (6)^3 = 216\ cm^3$
Use surface area formula:
$surface\ area\ of\ a\ cube$: $6(one\ side)^2 = 6(6)^2 = 6(36) = 216\ cm^2$

Example 3. Find the volume and surface area of this cube.

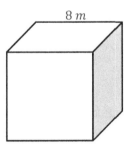

Solution: Use volume formula: $volume = (one\ side)^3$
Then: $volume = (one\ side)^3 = (8)^3 = 512\ m^3$
Use surface area formula:
$surface\ area\ of\ a\ cube$: $6(one\ side)^2 = 6(8)^2 = 6(64) = 384\ m^2$

Example 4. Find the volume and surface area of this cube.

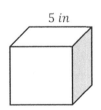

Solution: Use volume formula: $volume = (one\ side)^3$
Then: $volume = (one\ side)^3 = (5)^3 = 125\ in^3$
Use surface area formula:
$surface\ area\ of\ a\ cube$: $6(one\ side)^2 = 6(5)^2 = 6(25)$
$= 150\ in^2$

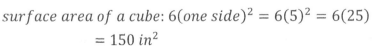

Rectangular Prisms

- A rectangular prism is a solid 3-dimensional object with six rectangular faces.

- The volume of a rectangular prism = $Length \times Width \times Height$

$$Volume = l \times w \times h$$
$$Surface\ area = 2 \times (wh + lw + lh)$$

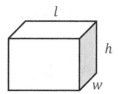

Examples:

Example 1. Find the volume and surface area of this rectangular prism.

Solution: Use volume formula: $Volume = l \times w \times h$

Then: $Volume = 7 \times 5 \times 9 = 315\ m^3$

Use surface area formula: $Surface\ area = 2 \times (wh + lw + lh)$

Then: $Surface\ area = 2 \times \big((5 \times 9) + (7 \times 5) + (7 \times 9)\big)$

$$= 2 \times (45 + 35 + 63) = 2 \times (143) = 286\ m^2$$

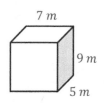

Example 2. Find the volume and surface area of this rectangular prism.

Solution: Use volume formula: $Volume = l \times w \times h$

Then: $Volume = 9 \times 6 \times 12 = 648\ m^3$

Use surface area formula: $Surface\ area = 2 \times (wh + lw + lh)$

Then: $Surface\ area = 2 \times \big((6 \times 12) + (9 \times 6) + (9 \times 12)\big)$

$$= 2 \times (72 + 54 + 108) = 2 \times (234) = 468\ m^2$$

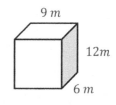

Example 3. Find the volume and surface area of this rectangular prism.

Solution: Use volume formula: $Volume = l \times w \times h$

Then: $Volume = 6 \times 9 \times 20 = 1080\ m^3$

Use surface area formula: $Surface\ area = 2 \times (wh + lw + lh)$

Then: $Surface\ area = 2 \times \big((6 \times 9) + (6 \times 20) + (9 \times 20)\big)$

$$= 2 \times (54 + 120 + 180) = 2 \times (354) = 708\ m^2$$

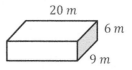

bit.ly/3nKm2GT

Find more at

Cylinder

- A cylinder is a solid geometric figure with straight parallel sides and a circular or oval cross-section.

$$Volume \ of \ a \ Cylinder = \pi(radius)^2 \times height, \ \pi \approx 3.14$$

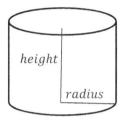

Examples:

Example 1. Find the volume of the follow Cylinder.

Solution: Use volume formula:

$Volume = \pi(radius)^2 \times height$

Then: $Volume = \pi(4)^2 \times 10 = 16\pi \times 10 = 160\pi$

$\pi = 3.14$, then: $Volume = 160\pi = 160 \times 3.14 = 502.4 \ cm^3$

So, the volume of the cylinder is $502.4 \ cm^3$.

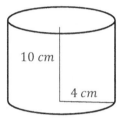

Example 2. Find the volume of the follow Cylinder.

Solution: Use volume formula:

$Volume = \pi(radius)^2 \times height$

Then: $Volume = \pi(5)^2 \times 8 = 25 \ \pi \times 8 = 200\pi$

$\pi = 3.14$, Then: $Volume = 200\pi = 628 \ cm^3$

So, the volume of the cylinder is $628 \ cm^3$.

Example 3. Find the volume of the follow Cylinder.

Solution: Use volume formula:

$Volume = \pi(radius)^2 \times height$

Then: $Volume = \pi(8)^2 \times 6 = 64 \ \pi \times 6 = 384\pi$

$\pi = 3.14$, Then: $Volume = 384\pi = 1205.76 \ cm^3$

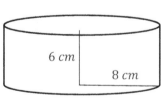

So, the volume of the cylinder is $1205.76 \ cm^3$.

Surface Area of Prisms and Cylinders

- **Prisms:** A prism is a polyhedron with two parallel and congruent bases. The sides (lateral faces) are parallelograms. The surface area is the total area covering the prism.

  Formula for the Surface Area of a Prism:
  $$Surface\ Area = 2 \times Area\ of\ Base + Perimeter\ of\ Base \times Height$$
  Formula for a rectangular prism:
  $$Surface\ Area = 2lw + 2lh + 2wh$$
  Where: l = length w = width h = height

- **Cylinders:** A cylinder has two congruent, parallel bases and a curved surface.

  Formula for the Surface Area of a Cylinder:
  $$Surface\ Area = 2\pi r^2 + 2\pi rh$$
  Where: r = radius of the base h = height of the cylinder

Examples:

Example 1. Consider a rectangular prism with length 3 units, width 2 units, and height 4 units. What is the surface Area of the prism?

Solution: Given that the length l is 3 units, the width w is 2 units, and the height h is 4 units, the surface area can be calculated as follows:

$Surface\ Area = 2lw + 2lh + 2wh \rightarrow SA = 2 \times 3 \times 2 + 2 \times 3 \times 4 + 2 \times 2 \times 4$

$$\rightarrow SA = 12 + 24 + 16 \rightarrow SA = 52$$

So, the surface area of the rectangular prism is 52 square units.

Example 2. Consider a cylinder with a radius 3 units and height 5 units. What is the surface Area of the cylinder?

Solution: Given that the radius r is 3 units and the height h is 5 units, the surface area can be calculated as follows:

$Surface\ Area = 2\pi r(r + h) \rightarrow SA = 2\pi 3(3 + 5) \rightarrow SA = 48\pi \rightarrow SA \approx 150.72$

So, the surface area of the cylinder is 48π square units. Note that π is approximately 3.14, so you can multiply this with 48, and we have approximately 150.72 square units.

bit.ly/462Ai2S

Find more at

Volume of Cones and Pyramids

- A cone is a three-dimensional geometric figure that has a flat surface and a curved surface pointed towards the top point called the vertex.

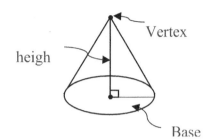

- Volume of a cone:

$$\frac{1}{3} \times \text{area of base} \times \text{height} = \frac{1}{3} \times B \times h = \frac{1}{3}\pi r^2 h$$

- A pyramid is a three-dimensional geometric figure that has a polygon base and triangular faces pointed towards the top point called the vertex.

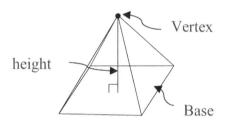

- Volume of a pyramid: $\frac{1}{3} \times \text{area of base} \times \text{height} = \frac{1}{3} \times B \times h$

Examples:

Example 1. Find the volume of the following cone. ($\pi = 3.14$)

Solution: Use the formula for the volume of cones: $\frac{1}{3}\pi r^2 h$

Substitute 7 for r and 14 for h:

$$V = \frac{1}{3}\pi (7)^2(14) \approx 718 \ cm^3$$

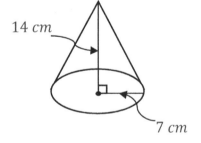

Example 2. Find the volume of the pyramid.

Solution: Volume of a pyramid $= \frac{1}{3} \times B \times h$, $B = 10 \times 8 = 80$.

Substitute 80 for B and 6 for h:

$$\frac{1}{3} \times B \times h = \frac{1}{3} \times 80 \times 6 = 160 in^3$$

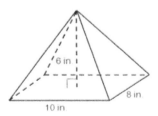

Surface Area of Pyramids and Cones

- **Surface Area of a Pyramid:** The surface area SA of a pyramid can be found using the formula:

$$SA = B + \left(\frac{1}{2}\right) \times P \times l$$

Where: B is the area of the base, P is the perimeter of the base, and l is the slant height.

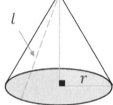

- **Surface Area of a Cone:** The surface area SA of a cone can be found using the formula:

$$SA = \pi r(r + l)$$

Where: r is the radius of the base, and l is the slant height.

Examples:

Example 1. There is a square pyramid with a base side length a of $6\ cm$ and a slant height l of $8\ cm$, what is the Surface Area of the square pyramid?

Solution: The base Area is: $B = a^2 = 6^2 = 36\ cm^2$

The perimeter is: $P = 4a = 4 \times 6 = 24\ cm$

The surface area will be: $SA = B + \left(\frac{1}{2}\right) \times P \times l = 36 + \left(\frac{1}{2}\right) \times 24 \times 8 = 132\ cm^2$

So, the surface area of the pyramid is $132\ cm^2$.

Example 2. There is a cone with a radius r of $5\ cm$ and a slant height l of $13\ cm$, what is the Surface Area of the cone?

Solution: The surface area can be calculated as follows:

$SA = \pi r(r + l) \rightarrow SA = \pi \times 5(5 + 13) \rightarrow SA = \pi \times 5 \times 18 \rightarrow SA = 90\pi \rightarrow SA \approx 282.6$

So, the surface area of the cone is 90π square centimeters. It is approximately $282.6\ cm^2$ (approximately $\pi = 3.14$).

Find more at bit.ly/40oXUxF

Volume of Spheres

- A sphere is a completely round three-dimensional object like a ball or a globe.

- The formula for the volume of a sphere is:

$$V = \frac{4}{3}\pi r^3$$

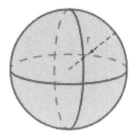

Examples:

Example 1. Find the volume of a sphere whose radius is $3\ cm$. ($\pi = 3.14$)

Solution: Given: radius, $r = 3\ cm$

Volume of a sphere formula: $\frac{4}{3}\pi r^3$

$$r = 3\ cm \rightarrow V = \frac{4}{3}\pi r^3 = \frac{4}{3}\pi(3)^3 = 113.04\ cm^3$$

Example 2. Find the volume of a sphere whose diameter is $12\ cm$. ($\pi = 3.14$)

Solution: Given, diameter: $12\ cm$

Then: $radius = \frac{diameter}{2} = \frac{12\ cm}{2} = 6\ cm$

Volume of a sphere formula: $V = \frac{4}{3}\pi r^3 \rightarrow V = \frac{4}{3}\pi(6)^3 = 904.32\ cm^3$

Example 3. Find the volume of a sphere whose diameter is $10\ in$. ($\pi = 3.14$)

Solution: Given, diameter: $10\ in$

Then: $radius = \frac{diameter}{2} = \frac{10\ in}{2} = 5\ in$

Volume of a sphere formula: $V = \frac{4}{3}\pi r^3 \rightarrow V = \frac{4}{3}\pi(5)^3 = 523.34\ in^3$

Sphere Surface Area

- A sphere can be described as a $3-D$ object whose surface area is the extent covered by its exterior. The surface of a sphere can be calculated using its radius, which is the distance from the sphere's center to any point on its surface. The sphere's surface 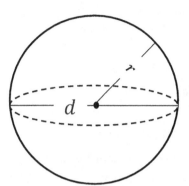 area formula is $4\pi r2$, where r is the radius. Another way to calculate the surface area is with regard to its diameter, which is the distance across the sphere. The formula for the sphere's surface area in terms of its diameter is $S = 4\pi(\frac{d}{2})^2$, where d represents the diameter. To calculate a sphere's surface area, you need to know its radius or diameter. Once you have that information, you can use one of the formulas above to determine the surface area.

Surface Area= $4\pi r^2$

Examples:

Example 1.   The radius of a sphere is 2 meters. Calculate its surface area.

Solution: The formula for the surface area of a sphere is $S = 4\pi(\frac{d}{2})^2$. The radius of the sphere is 2 meters, so its diameter becomes $d = 4$. Put 4 in the area formula:

$$S = 4\pi(\frac{d}{2})^2 = 4 \times 3.14 \times (\frac{4}{2})^2 = 50.24\ m^2$$

Example 2.   Find the surface area according to the figure below.

Solution: The formula for the surface area of a sphere is $S = 4\pi(\frac{d}{2})^2$. Insert the size of the diameter of the sphere into the formula and get the surface area.

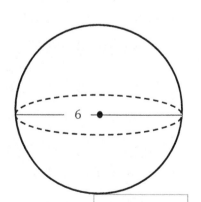

$$S = 4\pi(\frac{d}{2})^2 = 4 \times 3.14 \times (\frac{6}{2})^2 = 113.04$$

Solids and Their Cross Sections

- Every solid has surfaces that bound it, and when you make a "cut" or "slice" through a solid, you get a cross-section. The shape of this cross-section depends on the solid itself and the angle and position of the cut.

  - **Cube:** A perpendicular cut to a face gives a square cross-section. Diagonal slices, not through a vertex, create rectangles, while those through opposite vertices form hexagons.

  - **Cylinder:** A perpendicular cut to the base forms a circle, identical to the base. Slanted cuts parallel to the base yield ellipses, while cuts perpendicular to the curved surface create rectangles.

  - **Sphere:** Any slice through the center forms a circular cross-section. Its size ranges from small near the edge to the maximum at the center.

  - **Pyramid:** Horizontal slices create smaller base-like polygons that shrink upwards. A vertical center cut through a square or rectangular pyramid forms a triangle.

  - **Cone:** A perpendicular cut to the base creates a circle that shrinks closer to the tip. Slanted cuts parallel to the base form ellipses, while cuts perpendicular to the slanted side create parabolas.

Examples:

Example 1. Imagine you have a solid cylinder with a height of 10 *cm*. If you were to make a cut perpendicular to its base 7 *cm* above the base, what would the shape of the cross-section be?

Solution: Since the cut is made perpendicular to the base of the cylinder, the resulting cross-section would be a circle. The diameter of this circle would be the same as the diameter of the cylinder.

Example 2. Which of the following shapes would not be a cross-section of a cone?

  a.   b.   c.   d.

Solution: The shapes that could be a cross-section of a cone include a circle, triangle, ellipse and a parabola.

Therefore, the shape that would not be a cross-section of a cone from your options is a square (Option a).

Volume of a Truncated Cone

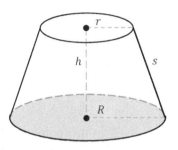

- A truncated cone, or a frustum of a cone, is a shape that you get when you slice off the top of a cone parallel to its base. This leaves you with two bases: a smaller circle on top and a larger circle on the bottom, with a curved surface connecting them.

- To find the volume of a frustum, you use the formula:

$$V = \left(\frac{1}{3}\right) \times \pi \times h \times \left(R^2 + r^2 + (R \times r)\right)$$

Where: V is the volume, h is the height of the frustum, R is the radius of the larger base, and r is the radius of the smaller base.

Examples:

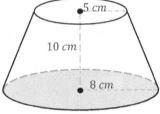

Example 1. find the volume of a truncated Cone:

Solution: Using the provided values in the formula ($\pi = 3.14$): $V = \left(\frac{1}{3}\right) \pi \times 10 \times (8^2 + 5^2 + 8 \times 5)$

$$\rightarrow V = \left(\frac{1}{3}\right) \times 10\pi \times (64 + 25 + 40) \rightarrow V = 430\pi \approx 1{,}350.2 \; cm^3$$

So, the volume of this a truncated Cone is approximately $1{,}350.2 \; cm^3$.

Example 2. If a cone has a radius of 8 *cm* and a height of 20 *cm*, and the top of the cone is cut off with a plane parallel to the base at a height of 15 *cm* from the base (forming a frustum), what is the volume of the resulting frustum?

Solution: We first find the radius of the smaller cone (which was cut off) using similar triangles, and it would be $\left(\frac{5}{20}\right) \times 8 = 2 \; cm$. Now we have a frustum with a smaller radius of 2 *cm*, a larger radius of 8 *cm*, and a height of 15 *cm*.

The volume V of a frustum of a cone is given by:

$$V = \left(\frac{1}{3}\right) \times \pi \times h \times \left(R^2 + r^2 + (R \times r)\right) \rightarrow V = \left(\frac{1}{3}\right) \times \pi \times 15 \times \left(8^2 + 2^2 + (8 \times 2)\right)$$

$$\rightarrow V = \left(\frac{1}{3}\right) \times 15\pi \times \left(64 + 4 + (16)\right) \rightarrow V = 420\pi \approx 1{,}318.8 \; cm^3$$

So, the volume of this a truncated Cone is approximately $1{,}318.8 \; cm^3$.

bit.ly/45YfBVC

Find more at

Chapter 10: Practices

✍ **Find the radius of each circle. Use your calculator's value of π. Round your answer to the nearest tenth.**

1) Circumference = 43.9 ft

3) Circumference = 94.2 mi

2) Circumference = 75.4 yd

4) Circumference = 12.6 yd

✍ **Find the circumference of each circle.**

5) Area = $49\pi\ mi^2$

6) Area = $81\pi\ in^2$

✍ **Find the area of each circle.**

7) Circumference = $12\pi\ yd$

8) Circumference = $26\pi\ in$

✍ **Find the area of each trapezoid.**

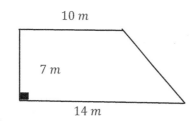

9)

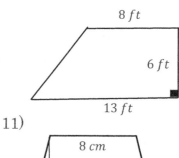

11)

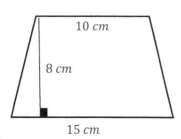

10)

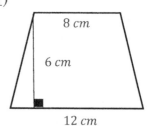

12)

🖋 **Find the area of each polygon. Round your answer to the nearest tenth.**

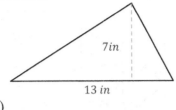

13)

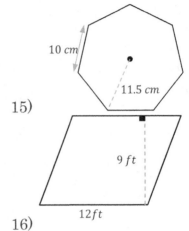

15)

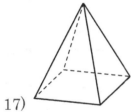

14)

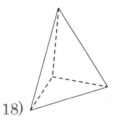

16)

🖋 **Create a net for the following figure.**

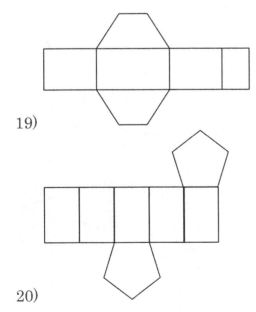

17)   18)

🖋 **Create a figure for the following net.**

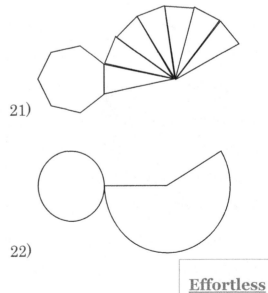

19)   21)

20)   22)

**Effortless
Math
Education**

Name each figure.

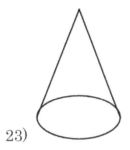

23)

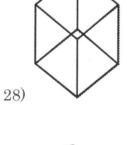

28)

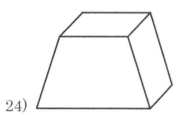

24)

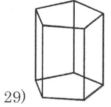

29)

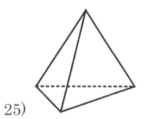

25)

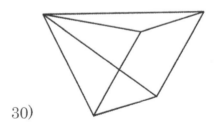

30)

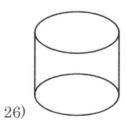

26)

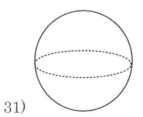

31)

27)

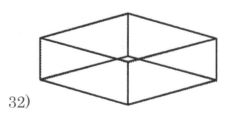

32)

✎ **Find the volume of each cube.**

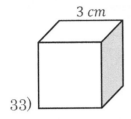

33)

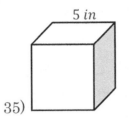

35)

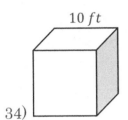

34)

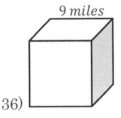

36)

✎ **Find the volume of each Rectangular Prism.**

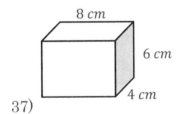

37)

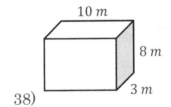

38)

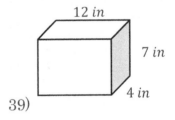

39)

✎ **Find the volume of each Cylinder. Round your answer to the nearest tenth. ($\pi = 3.14$)**

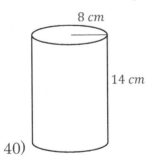

40)

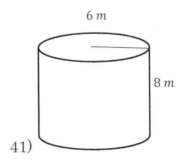

41)

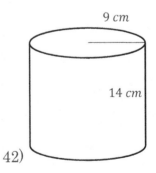

42)

Effortless
Math
Education

✎ **Find the area surface of each figure. Round your answer to nearest tenth. ($\pi = 3.14$)**

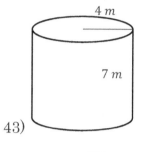

43)

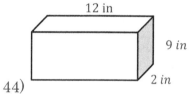

44)

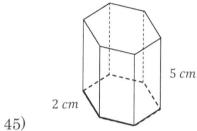

45)

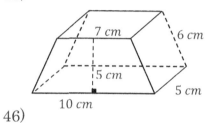

46)

✎ **Find the volume of each figure. Round your answer to nearest hundredth. ($\pi = 3.14$)**

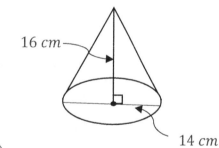

47)

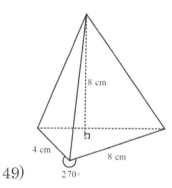

49)

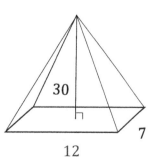

48)

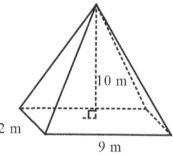

50)

Effortless Math Education

✏️ **Find the area surface of each figure. Round your answer to nearest tenth.** ($\pi = 3.14$)

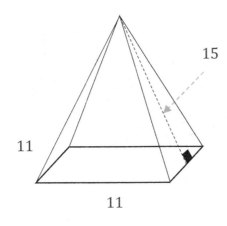

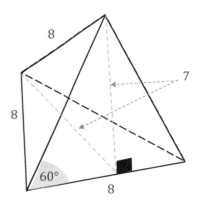

51)   52)

53) A cone with radius $6\,m$ and a slant height of $10\,m$.

54) Let's calculate: A slant height of a hexagonal pyramid $14\,cm$ tall, with a regular base measuring $6\,cm$ on each side and an apothem of length $5.2\,cm$.

✏️ **Find the volume of each Spheres. Round your answer to nearest hundredth.** ($\pi = 3.14$)

55) Diameter = $1.8\,ft$ 57) Radius = $10\,ft$

V= _____   V= _____

56) Diameter = $1.5\,cm$ 58) Radius = $12\,ft$

V= _____   V= _____

Effortless Math Education

✍ **Find the surface area each figure**.

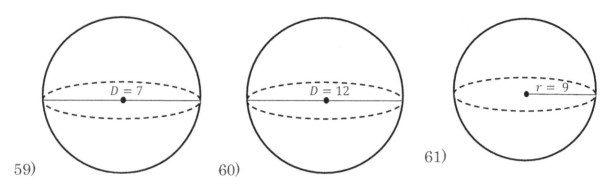

59)   60)   61)

✍ **Solve**.

62) If a rectangle is revolved around one of its sides, what is the solid produced?

63) If right triangle ABC, shown, was rotated around segment BC, what is the solid produced?

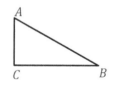

✍ **Draw the cross section of the given shapes.**

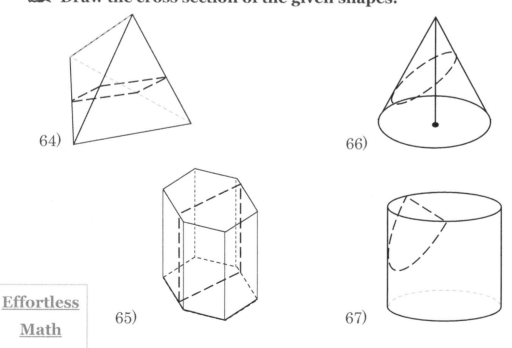

64)   66)

65)   67)

✎ **Find the volume of each figure. Round your answer to nearest hundredth. ($\pi = 3.14$)**

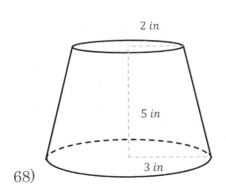

2 in

5 in

3 in

68)

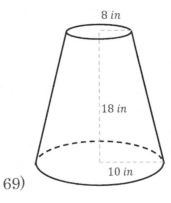

8 in

18 in

10 in

69)

✎ **Find the volume of** x**. Round your answer to nearest tenth. ($\pi = 3.14$)**

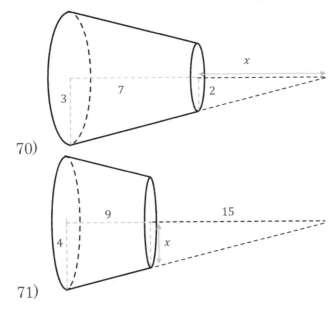

x

7

3

2

70)

9

15

4

x

71)

Effortless

Math

Education

Chapter 10: Answers

1) $7\,ft$

2) $12\,yd$

3) $15\,mi$

4) $2\,yd$

5) $14\pi\,mi$

6) $18\pi\,in$

7) $36\pi\,yd^2$

8) $169\pi\,in^2$

9) $84\,m^2$

10) $100\,cm^2$

11) $63\,ft^2$

12) $60\,cm^2$

13) $45.5\,in^2$

14) $468\,m^2$

15) $362.5\,cm^2$

16) $108\,ft^2$

17)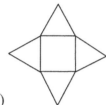

18)

19)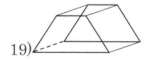

20)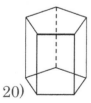

21)

22)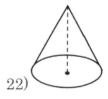

23) Cone

24) Trapezoidal prism

25) Triangular pyramid

26) Cylinder

27) Pentagonal pyramid

28) Square prism

29) Pentagonal prism

30) Rectangular pyramid

31) Sphere

32) Rectangular prism

33) $27 \ cm^3$

34) $1,000 \ ft^3$

35) $125 \ in^3$

36) $729 \ mi^3$

37) $192 \ cm^3$

38) $240 \ m^3$

39) $336 \ in^3$

40) $2,813.44 \ cm^3$

41) $904.32 \ m^3$

42) $3,560.76 \ cm^3$

43) $276.3 \ m^2$

44) $300 \ in^2$

45) $80.8 \ cm^2$

46) $245 \ cm^2$

47) $821 \ cm^3$

48) $840 \ cubic \ units$

49) $42.7 \ cm^3$

50) $60 \ m^3$

51) 451

52) 112

53) $301.4 \ m^2$

54) $345.6 \ cm^2$

55) $3.05 \ ft^3$

56) $1.77 \ cm^3$

57) $4,186.67 \ ft^3$

58) $7,234.56 \ ft^3$

59) 153.86

60) 452.16

61) 1017.36

62) Cylinder

63) Cone

64)

65)

66)

67)

68) $99.43 \ in^3$

69) $4596.96 \ in^3$

70) 14

71) 2.5

Time to Test

Time to refine your Geometry skills with a practice test.

Take a Geometry test to simulate the test day experience. After you've finished, score your test using the answer keys.

Before You Start

- You'll need a pencil and a calculator to take the test.
- **Scientific calculator is permitted for Geometry Test.**
- After you've finished the test, review the answer key to see where you went wrong.

Good Luck!

Geometry Practice
Test 1
2024

Total number of questions: 40

Total time: No time limit

Calculator is permitted for Geometry Test.

1) If angle $GQY = 130°$, find the angle CPQ.

   A. 230°

   B. 130°

   C. 50°

   D. 30°

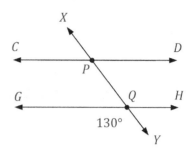

2) $\overrightarrow{QS}$ bisects $\angle PQR$. If $\angle RQS = 50°$, find $m\angle PQR$.

   A. 25°

   B. 50°

   C. 75°

   D. 100°

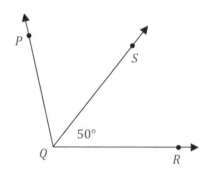

3) Three points that lie on a curve are:

   A. non-coplanar

   B. non-collinear

   C. collinear

   D. intersecting

4) $m\angle XOY$ is 45°. $\angle XOY$ is:

   A. an obtuse angle

   B. a right angle

   C. an acute angle

   D. a straight angle

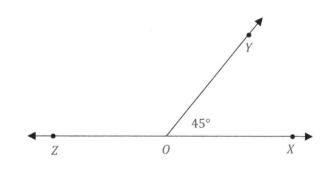

5) What is the equation of the line through $(-5, 8)$ and perpendicular to $y = \frac{3}{4}x + 6$?

A. $y = -\frac{4}{3}x + \frac{4}{3}$

B. $y = -\frac{4}{3}x + \frac{44}{3}$

C. $y = \frac{3}{4}x + \frac{47}{4}$

D. $y = -\frac{3}{4}x + \frac{17}{4}$

6) Find the slope of a line parallel to each given line: $y = -\frac{2}{5}x + 3$

A. $\frac{5}{2}$

B. $-\frac{5}{2}$

C. $\frac{2}{5}$

D. $-\frac{2}{5}$

7) Trapezoid $ABCD$ and $WXYZ$ are similar. Find WZ?

A. 23

B. 24

C. 33

D. 37.5

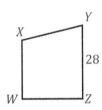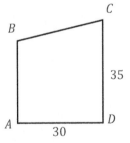

8) The volume of a cone is $200\ cm^3$. The height is $20\ cm$. Find the radius.

A. $\sqrt{30}$

B. 3.9

C. $\frac{\sqrt{30\pi}}{\pi}$

D. 2.52

9) Determine if the two triangles are congruent. If they are, state how you know.

    A. SSS

    B. ASS

    C. SAS

    D. ASA

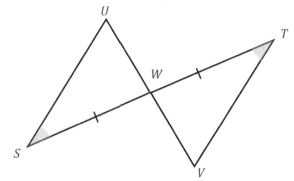

10) Find the volume of a sphere inscribed in a cube if each side of the cube is $8\ m$.

    A. 128π

    B. 85.33π

    C. 64π

    D. 21.33π

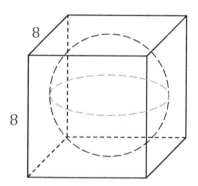

11) Find the length of TU for the coordinates:

$$T(2,7), U(7,21)$$

    A. 14

    B. $\sqrt{221}$

    C. 25

    D. $\sqrt{171}$

12) Find the slope of the line through each pair of points. $(12,-3), (13,-2)$

    A. 1

    B. -1

    C. $\frac{1}{5}$

    D. $-\frac{1}{5}$

13) Classify the triangle by its angles and sides.

A. Right Scalene

B. Acute isosceles

C. Obtuse scalene

D. Scalene isosceles

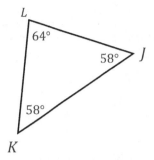

14) A cone has radius 6 *in* and height 14 *in* . A cylinder with radius 12 *in* has the same volume as the cone. What is the cylinder's height?

A. 14

B. 7

C. $\frac{7}{6}$

D. $\frac{6}{7}$

15) Order the sides of the triangle from shortest to longest.

A. $\overline{GH}, \overline{GI}, \overline{HI}$

B. $\overline{HI}, \overline{GI}, \overline{GH}$

C. $\overline{GI}, \overline{HI}, \overline{GH}$

D. $\overline{HI}, \overline{GH}, \overline{GI}$

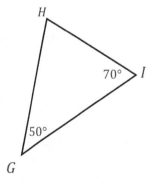

16) Find the value of x, if we extend GH from point G, the measure of the exterior angle at G is $2 + 18x$.

A. 110

B. 30

C. 7

D. 6

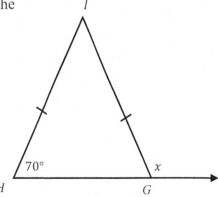

17) The water level of a swimming pool, 80 feet by 45 feet, is to be raised 5 inches. How many gallons of water must be added to accomplish this? (1 cubic foot = 7.48 gallons)

A. 18,000

B. 11,700

C. 11,220

D. 1,500

18) Which statement best describes the difference between a height and a bisector of a triangle?

A. A height is a line segment that splits an angle of the triangle in half, while a bisector splits a side into two equal parts.

B. A height divides the triangle into two triangles of equal area, while a bisector divides an angle into two equal angles.

C. A height is a line segment drawn from a vertex perpendicular to the opposite side, while a bisector is a line segment that divides an angle into two equal parts.

D. A height divides an angle into two equal parts, while a bisector is always a segment connecting a vertex to the midpoint of the opposite side.

19) Given the figure below, $SQ = 12$, $Ps = 25..5$, and $RT = TQ$. Find QT.

A. 30

B. 21.9

C. 15

D. 12.4

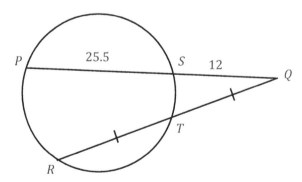

20) If the lengths of two sides of an isosceles triangle are 9 and 20, what is the perimeter of the triangle?

A. 29

B. 38

C. 49

D. 180

21) Find the area of the shaded region in the figure. If P is the center of the circle, $\overset{\frown}{QR} = 130°$, and $r = 7\ cm$.

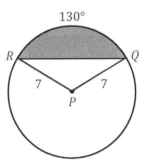

A. 18.8

B. 36.8

C. 55.7

D. 147.3

22) Tell the center and radius of the equation: $(x - 3)^2 + (y + 2)^2 = 20$

A. $(3, -2), r = 20$

B. $(3, -2), r = \sqrt{20}$

C. $(-2, 3), r = \sqrt{20}$

D. $(-2, 3), r = 20$

23) A rectangular box has dimensions 3 feet wide, 4 feet high, and 7 feet in length. Calculate the surface area of the box.

A. 28

B. 56

C. 84

D. 122

24) Find the length of the arc of a sector of 60° in a circle if the radius is 12. Find the area of the Sector.

    A. 4π, 24π

    B. 2π, 6π

    C. 6π, 2π

    D. 24π, 4π

25) Find the area of an equilateral triangle if each side is 10.

    A. 50

    B. 30

    C. $25\sqrt{3}$

    D. 25

26) Each side of an equilateral triangle is 14. Find the area of its inscribed and circumscribed circles.

    A. 17.1, 68.42

    B. 68.42, 17.1

    C. 51.28, 205.15

    D. 205.15, 51.28

27) One acute angle of a right triangle has measure $m°$. If $cos(m°) = \frac{4}{5}$, what is the value of $cot(m°)$?

    A. $\frac{3}{5}$

    B. $\frac{3}{4}$

    C. $\frac{5}{4}$

    D. $\frac{4}{3}$

28) Solve For y: if $UP = 8$, $PV = y$, $WP = 7$, $PX = 6$.

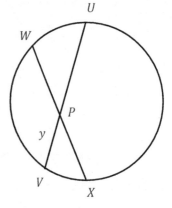

   A. 7

   B. 5.25

   C. 5

   D. 4.50

29) What is the angle of elevation of the sun when a tree 20 meters tall casts a shadow 30 meters long? Round to the nearest degree.

   A. 56°

   B. 48°

   C. 42°

   D. 34°

30) Given: $IJ = KL$, $\overline{LI} \perp \overline{IJ}$, $\overline{JK} \perp \overline{KL}$

   Prove: $\overline{LI} \parallel \overline{KJ}$

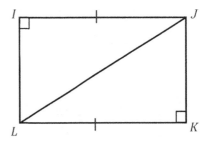

   Write your Answer.

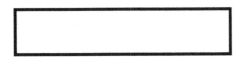

31) In a right triangle PQR, side PQ is $5 \ cm$ and angle $R = 40°$. Find the length of side QR.

   A. 3.21

   B. 5.96

   C. 6.53

   D. 7.78

32) Which graph is correct for this equation $(x - 5)^2 + (y - 3)^2 = 4$?

A.

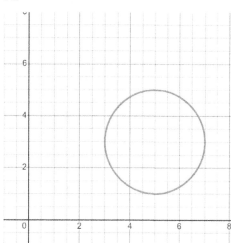

C.

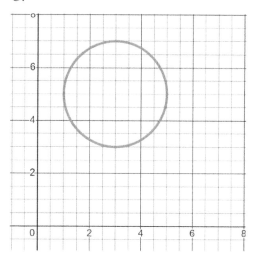

B.

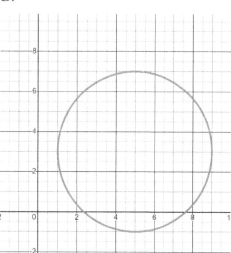

D.

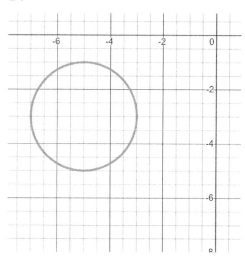

33) The apothem of a regular hexagon is $11\sqrt{3}$. Find the length of each side of the hexagon. Find the area of the hexagon.

A. 544.5

B. 816.5

C. $544.5\sqrt{3}$

D. 1633.5

34) Given the figure $EFGH$ is a trapezoid with $EF \parallel GH$, and $EF = 14$, $FG = 14$, angle $\angle F = 60°$ and $\angle H = 30°$. Find the area and perimeter of $EFGH$.

A. 169.68, 84

B. 254.52, 80.25

C. 254.52, 84

D. 486.45, 80.25

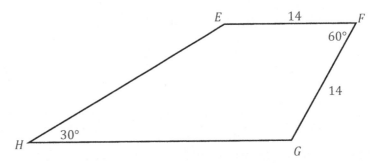

35) Find the sum of the areas of the shaded regions in the figure below:

$\overline{EF} = 9$, $\overline{FG} = 12$, $\widehat{GH} = 100°$ and $\widehat{EH} = 80°$, $(\pi = 3.14)$

A. 108

B. 68.6

C. 67.2

D. 54

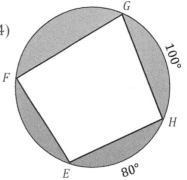

36) The lengths of the bases of a trapezoid are 10 and 24. What is the length of the median of the trapezoid?

A. 7

B. 12

C. 14

D. 17

37) According to the given figure, find OP and MP.

A. 6, 8

B. 8, 6

C. 6, 12

D. 30, 20

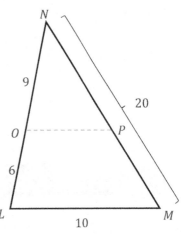

38) Which conditional's inverse is true?

    A. If two lines intersect to form an obtuse angle, then they are not perpendicular.

    B. If $m\angle Y$ is less than 40°, then $m\angle Y$ is acute.

    C. If point M is the midpoint of GH, then points G, M, and H are collinear

    D. If two rays are adjacent rays, then they have a common endpoint.

39) The sides of a rectangle are 18 and 36. What is the measure of the obtuse angle formed by the diagonals? Round to the nearest tenth.

    A. 26.6°

    B. 53.2°

    C. 126.8°

    D. 153.4°

40) Write a rule to describe the transformation.

    A. translation: 6 units up

    B. reflection across $y = -x$

    C. translation: 2 units right and 2 units up

    D. reflection across $y = -1$

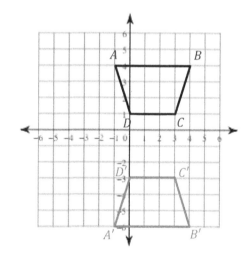

End of Geometry Practice Test 1

Geometry Practice
Test 2
2024

Total number of questions: 40

Total time: No time limit

Calculator is permitted for Geometry Test.

279

1) The areas of two similar triangles are 169 and 289. If a side of the smaller triangle is 11, how long is the corresponding side of the larger triangle?

    A. 17

    B. 14.4

    C. 14

    D. 13

2) If D is the midpoint of EF, $ED = 5x + 15$, and $DF = 8x - 24$, then what is EF?

    A. 160

    B. 80

    C. 52

    D. 13

3) Points $(3, 3)$ and $(9, w)$ lie on a line with slope $\frac{2}{3}$. What is the value of w?

    A. 7

    B. 4

    C. 3

    D. 2

4) Two lines in different planes that never meet are:

    A. perpendicular

    B. collinear

    C. skew

    D. parallel

5) The area of an equilateral triangle is $30\sqrt{3}$. Find the length of its sides and altitudes please.

    A. $2\sqrt{30}, 3\sqrt{10}$

    B. $3\sqrt{10}, 2\sqrt{30}$

    C. $2\sqrt{10}, 3\sqrt{30}$

    D. $3\sqrt{3}, 2\sqrt{10}$

6) What is the pre-image, Q, of $Q'(12, -5)$ using the transformation $(x, y) \rightarrow (4x, 5y)$?

    A. $(-3, 1)$

    B. $(-1, 3)$

    C. $(3, -1)$

    D. $(7, -1)$

7) Solve for the variables to make the lines parallel.

    A. $x = 85, y = 5.3$

    B. $x = 18, y = 9.5$

    C. $x = 5, y = 18$

    D. $x = 18, y = 5$

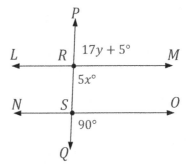

8) Find the slope of a line perpendicular to each given line: $y = -5x - 4$

    A. 5

    B. 0.5

    C. $\frac{1}{5}$

    D. $-\frac{1}{5}$

9) How many lines of symmetry does the following figure have and tell the rotational symmetry.

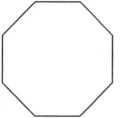 and S

A. Octagon: has 4 reflection lines of symmetry and a rotational symmetry of 90°.

   S-shaped: has no reflection lines of symmetry and a rotational symmetry of 180°.

B. Octagon: has 8 reflection lines of symmetry and a rotational symmetry of 45°.

   S-shaped: has no reflection lines of symmetry and a rotational symmetry of 180°.

C. Octagon: has 8 reflection lines of symmetry and a rotational symmetry of 45°.

   S-shaped: has 2 reflection lines of symmetry and a rotational symmetry of 90°.

D. Octagon: has 6 reflection lines of symmetry and a rotational symmetry of 45°.

   S-shaped: has no reflection lines of symmetry and a rotational symmetry of 90°.

10) The angle of depression from the top of a tower to a point P is 25°. The distance from P to the base, Q, of the tower is 90 m. How tall is the tower to the nearest meter?

A. 193 m

B. 82 m

C. 42 m

D. 38 m

11) Determine if the two triangles are congruent. If they are, state how you know.

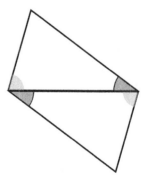

A. SSS

B. ASA

C. HL

D. AAS

12) A square pyramid with a base edge of 5 is inscribed in a cone with a height of 7. Determine the volume of both the pyramid and the cone. Round your answer to nearest of tenth.

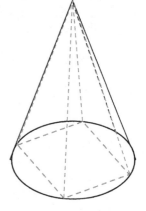

A. 58.3, 91.6

B. 91.6, 58.3

C. 58.3, 183.2

D. 50.3, 183.2

13) Given the figure, IJK is a right triangle, and $KL \perp IJ$, $JK \perp KI$, and sides as marked. Find the length of KL, JL and the area of triangle IJK.

A. 26.67, 35, 96

B. 26.67, 7.2, 96

C. 9.6, 12.8, 96

D. 96, 12.8, 9.6

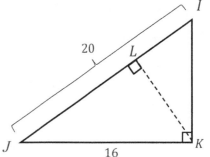

14) The volume of a cone is $450\ cm^3$ and the radius of the base is $6\ cm$. Find its altitude. Round your answer to nearest of centimeters

Write your Answer.

15) A semi-sphere is on a cylinder with the same radius $= 7\ cm$, and the height of the cylinder is $5\ cm$. Find the surface area and volume. Round your answer to nearest of ones

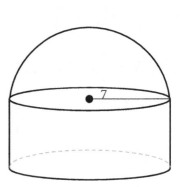

A. 266π, 474

B. 315π, 702π

C. 217π, 474

D. 217π, 702

16) In $\triangle XYZ$, the bisector of $\angle X$ (Line XW) creates $\angle 1$ and $\angle 2$.the sides are marked as follows. Determine the lengths of YW and ZW.

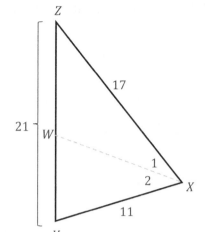

A. 8.25, 12.75

B. 12.75, 8.25

C. 10.5, 10.5

D. 7.4, 13.6

17) $\overrightarrow{CD}$ from $\angle ECD$ is tangent to the circle. $\overrightarrow{CE}$ intersects the circle creating a line segment $\overline{FG}$ with $EF = 14$ and $CF = 5$. Determine the length of the CD:

A. $\sqrt{14}$

B. $\sqrt{70}$

C. 35

D. 70

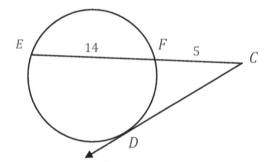

18) How do you determine one interior angle of a regular octagon? And one exterior angle?

A. 180°, 45°

B. 135°, 45°

C. 135°, 135°

D. 45°, 135°

19) Write the circle equation given the center $(-4, 2)$ and radius 6.

A. $(x + 4)^2 + (y + 2)^2 = \sqrt{6}$

B. $(x + 4)^2 + (y - 2)^2 = 6$

C. $(x + 4)^2 + (y - 2)^2 = 36$

D. $(x - 4)^2 + (y + 2)^2 = 6^2$

20) Classify the special quadrilateral. Then find the values of x and y.

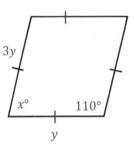

   A. 3, 110°

   B. 3, 70°

   C. 6, 70°

   D. 9, 110°

21) U, V, and W are all points of tangency. What is the perimeter of $\triangle ABC$?

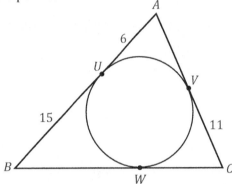

   A. 32

   B. 45

   C. 56

   D. 64

22) In triangle XYZ, it is known that $XY > XZ$ and $XY < YZ$. Order the angles from least to greatest measure.

   A. $\angle Y < \angle Z < \angle X$

   B. $\angle Z < \angle Y < \angle X$

   C. $\angle X < \angle Z < \angle Y$

   D. $\angle Y < \angle X < \angle Z$

23) If GHI is a right triangle: angle $I = 90°$, angle $H = 70°$, $IH = 10\sqrt{2}\ cm$. Find hypotenuse GH and side GI.

   A. 15.05, 14.14

   B. 15.05, 5.15

   C. 41.35, 38.83

   D. 14.14, 38.83

24) *LMNO* is a parallelogram. Given *LN* = 7, *LP* = 5, and *PM* = 3, determine the lengths *LQ* and *QN*.

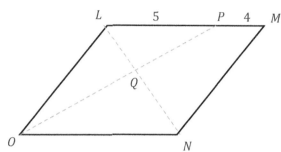

A. 1.5, 5.5

B. 2.5, 4.5

C. 3, 4

D. 5, 2

25) *EFGH* is a kite, *EF* = *EH* = 18. *PG* = 24 and *PH* = 14. So, find the length of *EG*, *FH*, and *FG*.

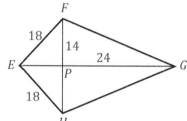

A. 46.8, 28, $2\sqrt{95}$

B. 48, 14, 27.8

C. 48, 28, 27.8

D. 35.3, 28, $2\sqrt{193}$

26) In a circle whose radius is 8, the area of a sector is (18π). Find the measure of the central angle of the sector and the length of the arc of the sector please.

A. 46.8, 28, $2\sqrt{95}$

B. 48, 14, 27.8

C. 48, 28, 27.8

D. 35.3, 28, $2\sqrt{193}$

27) According to the $\triangle FGH$, given *FI* = 6, *IG* = 4, and *GH* = 24, determine the lengths of *FH*, *HJ*, and *IJ*.

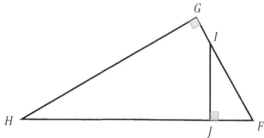

A. 30, $\frac{30}{13}$, $\frac{72}{13}$

B. 26, $\frac{308}{13}$, $\frac{72}{13}$

C. $2\sqrt{119}$, $\frac{308}{13}$, $\frac{72}{13}$

D. $2\sqrt{119}$, $\frac{30}{13}$, $\frac{72}{13}$

28) Find the measure of the given arc or variable.

A. 160°

B. 100°

C. 80°

D. 60°

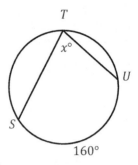

29) What are the coordinates of $\triangle ABC$, after a reflection in the line $y = -x$.

A. $A'(-3, -1), B'(0, -1), C'(0, -3)$

B. $A'(-1, -1), B'(0, 0), C'(-3, 0)$

C. $A'(-1, -3), B'(-1, 0), C'(-3, -3)$

D. $A'(0, -3), B'(0, -1), C'(0, -3)$

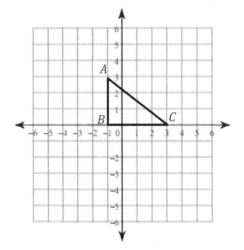

30) What are the coordinates of $\overline{AB}$, after a 45° rotation (counterclockwise) about the origin?

A. $A'(2, 1), B'(1, 4)$

B. $A'(-\sqrt{2}, 2\sqrt{2}), B'(\frac{3\sqrt{2}}{2}, \frac{5\sqrt{2}}{2})$

C. $A'(-1, 3), B'(-4, 1)$

D. $A'(2\sqrt{2}, -\sqrt{2}), B'(\frac{5\sqrt{2}}{2}, \frac{3\sqrt{2}}{2})$

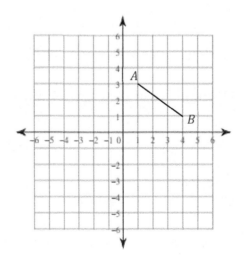

31) According to the figure below, $CE \perp AB$, D and F are midpoints. Find AC and GC.

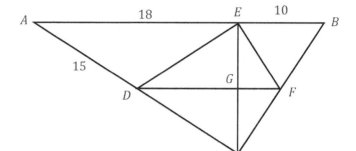

A. 15, 24

B. 30, 12

C. 30, 24

D. 15, 13

32) Given the statement "All Governors are over 35 years old," and the information that "Maria is 28 years old," which of the following conclusions is true??

A. Maria is a Governor.

B. Maria is not a Governor.

C. Maria might be a Governor.

D. Maria's age is unrelated to being a Governor.

33) Which of the following statements is logically equivalent to "If it snows, the roads become slippery"?

A. If the roads do not become slippery, then it doesn't snow.

B. If the roads become slippery, then it snows.

C. If it doesn't snow, the roads don't become slippery.

D. If it snows, the roads don't become slippery.

34) The radius of a circle is 22. The length of chord AB is 26. How far is AB from the center of the circle?

A. $3\sqrt{35}$

B. 22

C. $3\sqrt{7}$

D. $15\sqrt{7}$

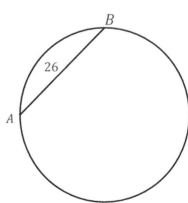

35) Given the following argument pattern:

$$b \rightarrow a$$

$$c \rightarrow b$$

Which conclusion logically follows from the given statements?

A. $a \rightarrow c$

B. $a \rightarrow b$

C. $c \rightarrow a$

D. $b \rightarrow c$

36) Two sides of a triangle are 15 and 18. Determine the range of possible values for the third side, z.

A. $15 < z < 18$

B. $15 \leq z \leq 18$

C. $33 \leq z \leq 3$

D. $3 < z < 33$

37) Order the sides of each triangle from Shortest to longest.

A. $\overline{HI}, \overline{GH}, \overline{GI}$

B. $\overline{HI}, \overline{GI}, \overline{GH},$

C. $\overline{GH}, \overline{HI}, \overline{GI}$

D. $\overline{GI}, \overline{GH}, \overline{HI}$

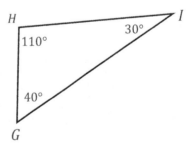

38) $IJKL$ is a parallelogram in the figure below, with the information given in the figure, find KM and $\frac{a\triangle IJN}{a\triangle MNK}$.

A. 3.6, 6.25

B. 3.6, 2.5

C. 2, 6.25

D. 2, 5

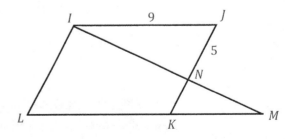

39) Given the truth values $p =$ true, $q =$ false, and $r =$ true, determine the truth value of the statement: $(\sim q \wedge p) \vee \sim r$.

A. True

B. False

C. Cannot be determined

D. Neither true nor false

40) $\overline{GH}$, $\overline{IJ}$, and $\overline{KL}$ intersect at Q. If $\angle G = 95°$, $\angle H = 55°$, $\angle K = 65°$, $\angle J = 50°$, and $\angle I = 55°$, what is the value of $\angle L$?

A. 15°

B. 30°

C. 40°

D. 65°

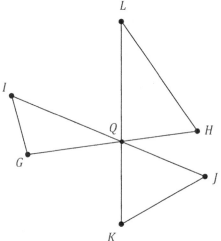

End of Geometry Practice Test 2

Geometry Practice Tests Answer Keys

Now, it's time to review your results to see where you went wrong and what areas you need to improve.

Geometry Practice Test 1				Geometry Practice Test 2			
1	B	21	B	1	B	21	D
2	D	22	B	2	A	22	A
3	B	23	D	3	A	23	C
4	C	24	A	4	C	24	B
5	A	25	C	5	A	25	D
6	D	26	C	6	C	26	A
7	B	27	D	7	D	27	B
8	C	28	B	8	C	28	C
9	D	29	D	9	B	29	A
10	B	30	-	10	C	30	B
11	B	31	B	11	B	31	B
12	A	32	A	12	A	32	B
13	B	33	C	13	C	33	A
14	C	34	B	14	12	34	A
15	B	35	C	15	C	35	C
16	D	36	D	16	A	36	D
17	B	37	A	17	B	37	C
18	C	38	D	18	B	38	A
19	C	39	C	19	C	39	D
20	C	40	D	20	B	40	B

Geometry Practice Test 1 Answers and Explanations

Geometry Practice Tests 1 Explanations

1. **Choice B is correct.**

Since CD is parallel to GH and XY is a transversal, angle GQY and angle CPQ are corresponding angles. Therefore, they are equal.

2. **Choice D is correct.**

Since QS bisects PQR, So: $\angle PQS = \angle RQS$

$\angle PRS = 50°$ and $\angle PQS = 50°$

Therefore: $\angle PQR = \angle RQS + \angle PQS \rightarrow \angle PQR = 50° + 50° \rightarrow \angle PQR = 100°$

3. **Choice B is correct.**

Three points that lie on a curve are non-collinear, meaning they don't all lie on a single straight line. If they were collinear, they would lie on a straight line.

4. **Choice C is correct.**

The measure of $\angle XOY$ is given as $45°$.

An angle that measures $45°$ is less than $90°$, so it is an acute angle.

5. **Choice A is correct.**

The slope of the given line is $\frac{3}{4}$. The slope of a line perpendicular to it will be the negative reciprocal, which is $m = -\frac{4}{3}$.

Using the point-slope form of a line:

$$y - y_1 = m(x - x_1) \rightarrow y - 8 = -\frac{4}{3}(x + 5) \rightarrow y = -\frac{4}{3}x - \frac{20}{3} + 8 \rightarrow y = -\frac{4}{3}x + \frac{4}{3}$$

So, the equation of the line is $y = -\frac{4}{3}x + \frac{4}{3}$.

6. Choice D is correct.

Parallel lines have the same slope. So, the slope of the line parallel to the given line is $-\frac{2}{5}$, the correct answer is option D.

7. Choice B is correct.

Since the trapezoids are similar, the ratio of their corresponding sides is the same.

$$\frac{AD}{WZ} = \frac{CD}{YZ} \rightarrow \frac{30}{WZ} = \frac{35}{28} \rightarrow WZ = 30 \times \frac{28}{35} \rightarrow WY = 24$$

So, $WY = 24$ units.

8. Choice C is correct.

The volume V of a cone is given by: $V = \frac{1}{3}\pi r^2 h$

Where: $r = $ radius, and $h = $ height

Volume is $200 \ cm^3$, and height is $20 \ cm$.

Plugging in the values:

$$200 = \frac{1}{3} \times \pi \times r^2 \times 20 \rightarrow r^2 = \frac{200 \times 3}{20 \times \pi} \rightarrow r^2 = \frac{30}{\pi} \rightarrow r^2 \approx 9.6 \rightarrow r = \sqrt{9.6} \approx 3.09$$

9. Choice D is correct.

Considering the triangles SUW and WTV:

We have a shared angle, $\angle W$, since it's an angle in both triangles. (According to Vertical Angles Theorem)

$\angle S$ is equal to $\angle T$. And $\overline{SW}$ is equal to $\overline{WT}$.

The given conditions fit the criteria for the Angle-Side-Angle (ASA) postulate of congruence. With ASA, if two angles and the included side of one triangle are congruent to two angles and the included side of another triangle, then the two triangles are congruent.

Thus, $\triangle SUW$ is congruent to $\triangle WTV$ by the ASA postulate.

10. Choice B is correct.

Sphere in a Cube: Side of cube is $8\ m$. The diameter of the inscribed sphere is equal to the side of the cube. So, the radius $r = \dfrac{8}{2} = 4$.

Volume of the sphere: $V = \dfrac{4}{3}\pi r^3 = \dfrac{4}{3}\pi(4^3) = \dfrac{256}{3}\pi \approx 85.33\pi$

Volume of the inscribed sphere is approximately $85.33\pi\ m^3$.

11. Choice B is correct.

Using the distance formula:

$$TU = \sqrt{(7-2)^2 + (21-7)^2} \rightarrow TU = \sqrt{5^2 + 14^2} \rightarrow TU = \sqrt{25 + 196} \rightarrow TU = \sqrt{221}$$

12. Choice A is correct

The slope m is given by: $m = \dfrac{y_2 - y_1}{x_2 - x_1}$

Using the slope formula: $m = \dfrac{-2+3}{13-12} \rightarrow m = 1$

13. Choice B is correct.

The triangle has two angles that are equal, which makes it an isosceles triangle. Also, all angles are less than $90°$, so it's an acute triangle. Therefore, triangle JKL is an acute isosceles triangle.

14. Choice C is correct.

Given: $r_{cone} = 6\ in$, and $h_{cone} = 14\ in$

Volume of a cone: $V = \dfrac{1}{3}\pi r^2 h \rightarrow V = \dfrac{1}{3}\pi \times 6^2 \times 14 \rightarrow V = 168\pi\ in^3$

Given: $r_{cylinder} = 12\ in$, and $V_{cylinder} = 168\pi\ in^3$ (since it's equal to the volume of the cone)

Volume of a cylinder: $V = \pi r^2 h \rightarrow 168\pi = \pi \times 12^2 \times h \rightarrow h = \dfrac{168\pi}{144\pi} \rightarrow h = \dfrac{7}{6}\ in$

So, the height of the cylinder is $\dfrac{7}{6}$ or 1.17 inches.

15. Choice B is correct.

In any triangle, the side opposite the largest angle is the longest, and the side opposite the smallest angle is the shortest. Given the angles:

Shortest side $=$ Side opposite $(50°) = (\overline{HI})$

Middle side $=$ Side opposite $60°$ (since the sum of angles in a triangle is $180°$ and $180 - 50 - 70 = 60 = (\overline{GI})$

Longest side $=$ Side opposite $70° = (\overline{GH})$

So, the order from shortest to longest is: $\overline{HI}, \overline{GI}, \overline{GH}$

16. Choice D is correct.

In triangle GHI, since $HI = GI$, it's an isosceles triangle. All angles in an isosceles triangle with a base angle of $70°$ are $70°$, $70°$, and $40°$. The exterior angle at G will be:

Exterior $\angle G = 180° - 70° = 110°$

Setting this equal to the given expression: $2 + 18x = 110 \rightarrow 18x = 108 \rightarrow x = 6$

17. Choice B is correct.

Given: Length $= 80$ feet, width $= 45$ feet, and height to be raised $= 5$ inches $= \frac{5}{12}$ feet

Volume to be added: $V = 80 \times 45 \times \frac{5}{12} \rightarrow V = 1,500$

To convert to gallons: $V = 1,500 \times 7.48 = 11,700 \ gl$

So, $11,700$ gallons of water must be added.

18. Choice C is correct.

A height of a triangle is a segment from a vertex that is perpendicular to the opposite side (or to the line containing the opposite side). It represents the height of the triangle from that vertex. A bisector of a triangle is a segment from a vertex that divides the opposite side into two segments that have the same ratio as the two adjacent sides.

19. Choice C is correct.

If two secant segments are drawn from a point outside a circle, then: $QP \times SQ = QR \times TQ$

Given: $SQ = 12$, $PS = 25.5$, and $RT = TQ$

We also have: $QP = PS + SQ = 25.5 + 12 = 37.5$

And given: $RT = TQ$, $QR = RT + TQ = 2 \times RT$

Based on the formula, plug in our known values:

$$QP \times SQ = QR \times TQ \rightarrow 37.5 \times 12 = 2RT \times RT \rightarrow 450 = 2RT^2 \rightarrow RT = \sqrt{225} \rightarrow RT$$
$$= 15$$

So, the length of segment RT (and TQ since they're equal) is 15 units.

20. Choice C is correct.

To solve the problem, we first need to understand the properties of an isosceles triangle. An isosceles triangle has two sides of equal length.

Now, Let's analyze the two possible scenarios for our isosceles triangle:

If the two equal sides are each 9 units:

The sum of these two sides is $9 + 9 = 18$. For this to be an isosceles triangle with the third side being 20 units, 18 should be greater than 20. This is not true, so this cannot be our triangle.

If the two equal sides are each 20 units:

The sum of these two sides is $20 + 20 = 40$. The third side is 9 units. Since $40 > 9$, this is a valid isosceles triangle by the triangle inequality theorem.

Therefore, the perimeter for this valid isosceles triangle is:

Perimeter $= 20 + 20 + 9 = 49$ units.

21. Choice B is correct.

The formula for area of a Segment of a Circle is as follows: $Area = \frac{1}{2}r^2(\theta(\frac{\pi}{180°}) - sin\,\theta)$

Where: r = radius, θ = cantral angle (in radius)

Calculate the area of the segment, using the formula:

$$A = \frac{1}{2}(7)^2\left(130°\left(\frac{\pi}{180°}\right) - sin\,130°\right) \rightarrow A = \frac{49}{2}(2.27 - 0.77) \rightarrow A = 24.5 \times 1.5$$

$$\rightarrow A \approx 36.75$$

Thus, the area of the segment between $\overline{QR}$ and $\overparen{QR}$ is approximately $36.75\ cm^2$.

22. Choice B is correct.

The general equation of a circle $is\ (x - h)^2 + (y - k)^2 = r^2$, where (h, k) is the center and r is the radius.

Given the equation $(x - 3)^2 + (y + 2)^2 = 20$:

So, Center is $(3, -2)$

Radius is $\sqrt{20}$ or approximately 4.47 units.

23. Choice D is correct.

The surface area (SA) of a rectangular box is given by:

$$SA = 2lw + 2lh + 2wh$$

Where: l = length, w = width, and h = height

Plugging in the given values:

$$SA = 2(7 \times 3) + 2(7 \times 4) + 2(3 \times 4) \rightarrow SA = 42 + 56 + 24 = 122\ ft^2$$

24. Choice A is correct.

Arc Length: $L = \frac{\theta}{360} \times 2\pi r$

Sector Area: $A = \frac{\theta}{360} \times \pi r^2$

Using $\theta = 60°$ and $r = 12$:

$L = \frac{60}{360} \times 2\pi \times 12 \rightarrow L = 4\pi$ units.

$A = \frac{60}{360} \times \pi \times 12^2 = 24\pi$ square units.

25. Choice C is correct.

Equilateral Triangle Area:

For an equilateral triangle with side s: $Area = \frac{\sqrt{3}}{4} \times s^2$

Using $s = 10$: $Area = \frac{\sqrt{3}}{4} \times 10^2 \rightarrow Area = 25\sqrt{3}$

Therefore, the area of the triangle is $25\sqrt{3}$ square units.

26. Choice C is correct.

Given an equilateral triangle with each side measuring 14 units, we can find the area of its inscribed and circumscribed circles.

Inscribed circle: First, let's find the radius r of the incircle. In an equilateral triangle, the radius of the inscribed circle (inradius) can be found using, $r = \frac{a}{2\sqrt{3}}$.

Where a is the side length of the triangle.

Plugging in the given side length: $r = \frac{14}{2\sqrt{3}} = \frac{7}{\sqrt{3}} = 4.04$ units

Now, the area of the inscribed circle is:

$$A = \pi r^2 = \pi \times \left(\frac{7}{\sqrt{3}}\right)^2 = \frac{49}{3}\pi = 16.33\pi = 51.28 \text{ Square units}$$

Circumscribed Circle: For an equilateral triangle, the radius R of the circumscribed circle (circumradius) is, $R = \frac{a}{\sqrt{3}}$.

Using the given side length: $R = \frac{14}{\sqrt{3}} = 8.08$ units

The area of the circumscribed circle is:

$$A = \pi R^2 = \pi \left(\frac{14}{\sqrt{3}}\right)^2 = 65.33\pi = 205.15 \text{ Square units}$$

The area of the inscribed circle is approximately 16.33π or 51.28 square units.

The area of the circumscribed circle is approximately 65.33π or 205.15 square units.

27. Choice D is correct.

Using the Pythagorean identity:

$$sin(m°) = \sqrt{1 - cos(m°)^2} \rightarrow sin(m°) = \sqrt{1 - \left(\frac{4}{5}\right)^2} \rightarrow sin(m°) = \sqrt{\frac{9}{25}} \rightarrow sin(m°) = \frac{3}{5}$$

Now, $cot(m°)$ is the reciprocal of $tan(m°)$ and $tan(m°) = \frac{sin(m°)}{cos(m°)}$:

$$cot(m°) = \frac{cos(m°)}{sin(m°)} \rightarrow cot(m°) = \frac{\frac{4}{5}}{\frac{3}{5}} \rightarrow cot(m°) = \frac{4}{3}$$

So, the value of $cot(m°)$ is $\frac{4}{3}$.

28. Choice B is correct.

Using the property of intersecting chords:

$$UP \times PV = WP \times PX$$

From this, we can find y:

$$8 \times y = 7 \times 6 \rightarrow y = \frac{42}{8} = 5.25$$

The length of $\overline{PV}$ is 5.25 units.

29. Choice D is correct.

Height of the tree: $h = 20$ meters

Length of the shadow: $s = 30$ meters

The angle of elevation, (θ), can be found using the tangent function:

$$tan\, \theta = \frac{h}{s} \rightarrow tan\, \theta = \frac{20}{30} \rightarrow tan\, \theta = \frac{2}{3}$$

Using the inverse tangent function:

$$\theta = \tan^{-1}\left(\frac{2}{3}\right)$$

Using a calculator: $\theta \approx 33.69°$

Rounding to the nearest degree, the angle of elevation θ is 34°.

So, the angle of elevation of the sun is 34°.

30. The answer is:

Statement	Reason
1. $IJ = KL, \overline{LI} \perp \overline{IJ}, \overline{JK} \perp \overline{KL}$	1. Given
2. $\angle I$ and $\angle K$ are right angles	2. Definition of perpendicular lines
3. $\angle L$ is congruent to $\angle K$	3. All right angles are congruent
4. $LJ = LJ$	4. Reflection POE
5. $\triangle IJL \cong \triangle JKL$	5. $HL \cong$
6. $\angle ILJ \cong \angle LJK$	6. Definition of Congruent Triangles
7. $\overline{LI} \parallel \overline{KJ}$	7. Alternate Interior Angle Theorem

Thus, using the two-column proof, we've proven that LI is parallel to KJ.

31. Choice B is correct.

Using the tangent function:

$$\tan(R) = \frac{PQ}{QR} \rightarrow \tan 40° = \frac{5}{QR} \rightarrow QR = \frac{5}{0.839} = 5.96$$

QR is approximately $5.96\ cm$.

32. Choice A is correct.

Plot the center The center is (5,3).

Find the radius: The radius is $\sqrt{4} = 2$.

Count the radius in each direction from the center to find points on the edge: From the center (5,3), move 2 units in all directions to plot points on the circle.

Now, sketch the circle.

Therefore, the correct graph for a circle with center (5,3) and radius 2 is option A.

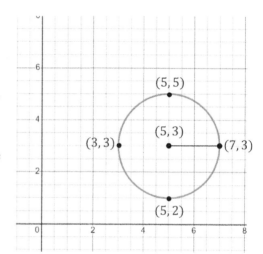

33. Choice C is correct.

For a regular hexagon with apothem a:

Side length: $s = a\sqrt{3}$

Area: $A = \frac{3}{2} \times s \times a$

Then, using $a = 11\sqrt{3}$: $S = 11\sqrt{3} \times \sqrt{3} = 33$ units

Then plug 33, in Area formula: $A = \frac{3}{2} \times 33 \times 11\sqrt{3} = 544.5\sqrt{3}$ square units.

34. Choice B is correct.

For solving this problem, we can divide this trapezoid to $\triangle EFG$ and $\triangle EGH$:

Now, solve for $\triangle EFG$:

Since triangle EFG has two equal sides, it's an isosceles triangle.

To find $\angle E'$ and $\angle G'$. In an isosceles triangle, the angles opposite the equal sides are also equal. Therefore, $\angle E'$ and $\angle G'$ are congruent.

To find side EG:

Since $\triangle EFG$ is equilateral, all sides are equal.

Therefore, $EG = EF = FG = 14\ cm$.

Now, solve for $\triangle EGH$.

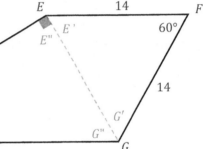

Since EF is parallel to GH, $\angle G = 180° - 60° = 120°$ and $\angle E = 180° - 30° = 150°$.

So: $\angle G = \angle G' + \angle G'' \rightarrow 120° = 60° + \angle G'' \rightarrow \angle G'' = 60°$

Then: $\angle E = \angle E' + \angle E'' \rightarrow 150° = 60° + \angle E'' \rightarrow \angle E'' = 90°$

Triangle EGH is a $30, 60, 90$ right triangle. For a $30, 60, 90$ triangle, the ratios of the sides are:

1. Side opposite $30°$ is half the hypotenuse.

2. Side opposite $60°$ is $\sqrt{3}$ times the side opposite the $30°$ angle.

3. Side opposite $90°$ (hypotenuse) is twice the side opposite the $30°$ angle.

Given EG (opposite the $90°$ angle) is $14\ cm$:

1. HG (side opposite the $30°$ angle): $HG = 2EG \rightarrow HG = 2 \times 14 \rightarrow HG = 28\ cm$

2. EH (side opposite the $60°$ angle): $EH = EG \times \sqrt{3} \rightarrow EH = 14\sqrt{3} \rightarrow EH \approx 24.25\ cm$ (Rounded to two decimal places)

So, EH is approximately $24.25\ cm$, and $HG = 28\ cm$.

Trapezoid perimeter:

$$P = EF + FG + HG + HE$$

Now calculate it:

$$P = 14 + 14 + 28 + 24.25 \rightarrow P = 80.25 \ cm$$

Trapezoid Area:

$$A = \frac{1}{2}(EF + HG)h$$

We need to calculate the height of the trapezoid. Since the height of the trapezoid is equal to height of the equilateral triangle, So, to find the height (or altitude) of triangle EFG:

Let's drop a perpendicular from G to EF, splitting EF into two equal parts, each $7 \ cm$. Call the point where the perpendicular meets EF as P.

Triangle GPE is a $30, 60, 90$ right triangle, therefore:

$$GP = EP\sqrt{3} \rightarrow GP = 7\sqrt{3} \rightarrow GP = 12.12 \ cm$$

Thus, the height (altitude) GP of the triangle is approximately $12.12 \ cm$.

Noe we can calculate the area of trapezoid:

$$A = \frac{1}{2}(14 + 28)12.12 \rightarrow A = \frac{42 \times 12.12}{2} \rightarrow A = \frac{509.04}{2} \rightarrow A = 254.52 \ cm^2$$

Therefore, the area is $254.52 \ cm^2$. And the perimeter is $80.25 \ cm$.

35. Choice C is correct.

Since the measure of an inscribed angle is half the measure of its intercepted arc. So:

$m\angle EFG = \frac{1}{2}\overset{\frown}{GE}$, and $GE = GH + HE = 100° + 80° = 180°$. Then:

$$m\angle EFG = \frac{1}{2} \times 180° = 90°$$

Now, since EFG is a right triangle and EG is equal to the diameter of circle, we can use the Pythagorean theorem to find the length of the diameter.

$$EG^2 = EF^2 + FG^2 \rightarrow EG^2 = 9^2 + 12^2 \rightarrow EG = \sqrt{225} = 15$$

The radius r is half of the diameter: $EG = d = 2r \rightarrow 15 = 2r \rightarrow r = 7.5$

Now, we can determine the area of the segments GH and EH:

$$Area = \frac{1}{2}r^2 \left(\theta\left(\frac{\pi}{180°}\right) - \sin\theta\right)$$

$$A_{GH} = \frac{1}{2}(7.5)^2 \left(\frac{100°\pi}{180°} - \sin 100°\right) = \frac{56.25}{2} \times (1.744 - 0.984) = 28.125 \times 0.76 = 21.375$$

$$A_{EH} = \frac{1}{2}(7.5)^2 \left(\frac{80°\pi}{180°} - \sin 80°\right) = \frac{56.25}{2} \times (1.394 - 0.984) = 28.125 \times 0.41 = 11.531$$

And for area of the segments EF and FG, we can calculate the area of triangle EFG and subtract it from the area of the semicircle:

The area of triangle EFG:

$$A_{EFG} = \frac{1}{2}bh = \frac{1}{2} \times 9 \times 12 = 54$$

The Sum of the area segment of EF and FG:

$$A_{EF} + A_{FG} = \frac{1}{2}\pi r^2 - A_{EFG} = \frac{3.14 \times 56.25}{2} - 54 = 88.313 - 54 = 34.313$$

Combine the areas of the segments:

Shaded area $= A_{GH} + A_{EH} + (A_{EF} + A_{FG}) = 21.375 + 11.531 + 34.313 = 67.219$

Therefore, the shaded are in the figure is 67.219 Square units.

36. Choice D is correct.

The median (or mid-segment) of a trapezoid is the segment that connects the midpoints of the non-parallel sides. Its length is the average of the lengths of the bases.

$b_1 = 10$ and $b_2 = 24$. So, Median (M) is given by:

$$M = \frac{b_1 + b_2}{2} \rightarrow M = \frac{10 + 24}{2} \rightarrow M = 17$$

So, the length of the median of the trapezoid is 17 units.

37. Choice A is correct.

OP is parallel to LM. we can use similar triangles to find the lengths of OP and MP.

Using the properties of similar triangles: $\frac{OP}{LM} = \frac{ON}{LN} \rightarrow \frac{OP}{10} = \frac{9}{9+6} \rightarrow OP = \frac{90}{15} \rightarrow OP = 6$

Similarly: $\frac{MP}{MN} = \frac{LO}{LN} \rightarrow \frac{MP}{20} = \frac{6}{9+6} \rightarrow MP = \frac{120}{15} \rightarrow MP = 8$

Therefore, the length of OP is 6 units. And MP is 8 units.

38. Choice D is correct.

To find the inverse of a conditional statement, you negate both the hypothesis and the conclusion. Let's find the inverses for each of the options:

A) Inverse: If two lines do not intersect to form an obtuse angle, then they are perpendicular.

B) Inverse: If $m\angle Y$ is not less than 40°, then $m\angle Y$ is not acute.

C) Inverse: If point M is not the midpoint of GH, then points G, M, and H are not collinear.

D) Inverse: If two rays are not adjacent rays, then they do not have a common endpoint.

Now, let's evaluate the truth of the inverses:

A) This is not universally true. Just because two lines do not intersect to form an obtuse angle doesn't mean they are perpendicular. They could form an acute angle.

B) This is not necessarily true. An acute angle is defined as an angle that is less than 90°. If $m\angle Y$ is not less than 40°, then its measurement is 40° or more. However, this range (40° or more) includes both acute angles (those between 40° and 90°) and angles that are not acute (90° and above).

C) This is not necessarily true. Even if point M is not the midpoint, the points could still be collinear.

D) This is true. If two rays aren't adjacent, they don't share a common endpoint.

The inverse that is true, is option D.

39. Choice C is correct.

The diagonal, d , can be found using the Pythagorean theorem:

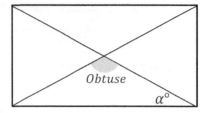

$$d = \sqrt{l^2 + w^2} \rightarrow d = \sqrt{36^2 + 18^2} \rightarrow d = \sqrt{1{,}296 + 324}$$
$$\rightarrow d = \sqrt{1{,}620} \rightarrow d = 40.25$$

The cosine of the angle between the diagonal and the length is:

$$\cos \alpha = \frac{l}{d} \rightarrow \cos \alpha = \frac{36}{40.25} \rightarrow \cos \alpha = 0.894$$

Using the inverse cosine function:

$$\alpha = \cos^{-1} \frac{36}{40.25} \rightarrow \alpha = 26.6°$$

The obtuse angle formed by the diagonals is: $180° - 26.6° - 26.6° = 126.8°$

40. Choice D is correct.

Shape ABCD is reflected across $y = -1$ and shape $A'B'C'D'$ is made.

Geometry Practice Tests 2 Explanations

1. Choice B is correct.

The areas of similar triangles are proportional to the square of the ratio of their corresponding sides. If the areas of the two similar triangles are $A_1 = 169$ and $A_2 = 289$, and a side of the smaller triangle $s_1 = 11$, then the corresponding side of the larger triangle s_2 can be found using the following formula:

$$\frac{A_1}{A_2} = \left(\frac{s_1}{s_2}\right)^2$$

Substituting the given values, we have:

$$\left(\frac{169}{2189}\right) = \left(\frac{11}{s_2}\right)^2 \rightarrow \left(\frac{169}{2189}\right) = \frac{121}{s_2^2}$$

Now solve for s_2:

$$S_2^2 = \frac{289 \times 11}{169} = \frac{34,969}{169} \approx 207$$

Finally, take the square root to find s_2:

$$S_2 = \sqrt{207} \approx 14.4$$

So, the length of the corresponding side of the larger triangle is approximately 14.4 units.

2. Choice A is correct.

Since D is the midpoint of EF, ED=DF. Thus:

$$5x + 15 = 8x - 24 \rightarrow 3x = 39 \rightarrow x = 13$$

Solving for x gives $x = 13$.

Now, $EF = ED + DF$: $EF = (5(13) + 15) + (8(13) - 24) \rightarrow EF = 80 + 80 \rightarrow EF = 160$

Therefore, the length of EF is 160.

3. Choice A is correct.

Using the formula for slope: $m = \frac{y_2 - y_1}{x_2 - x_1}$

Given: $m = \frac{2}{3}, x_1 = 3, y_1 = 3, x_2 = 9$

Now, substitute in the slop formula: $\frac{2}{3} = \frac{w - 3}{9 - 3} \rightarrow w - 3 = \frac{2 \times 6}{3} \rightarrow w = 4 + 3 \rightarrow w = 7$

So, the value of w is 7.

4. Choice C is correct.

Lines that are in different planes and never intersect are called skew lines. They are neither parallel nor perpendicular because those concepts apply to lines within the same plane.

5. Choice A is correct.

Equilateral Triangle Sides and Altitudes: For an equilateral triangle with area A: $A = \frac{\sqrt{3}}{4} s^2$

Using $A = 30\sqrt{3}$: $s^2 = \frac{4 \times 30\sqrt{3}}{\sqrt{3}} \rightarrow s^2 = 120 \rightarrow s^2 = 2\sqrt{30}$

That's the side length of the equilateral triangle.

Now for the altitude, using the Area formula: $A = \frac{1}{2} bh$

Substitute values: $30\sqrt{3} = \frac{1}{2} \times 2\sqrt{30} \times h \rightarrow h = \frac{30\sqrt{3}}{\sqrt{30}} \rightarrow h = 3\sqrt{10}$

So, the side length of the equilateral triangle is $2\sqrt{30}$ units and its altitude is $3\sqrt{10}$ units.

6. Choice C is correct.

Given: $x' = 4x, y' = 5y$, and $x' = 12, y' = -5$

We can write two equation and solve for x and y: $4x = 12 \rightarrow x = \frac{12}{4} \rightarrow x = 3$

$$5y = -5 \rightarrow y = \frac{15}{5} \rightarrow y = -1$$

So, the pre-image Q is $(3, -1)$.

7. Choice D is correct.

Given that lines LM and NO are parallel and line PQ intersects them, angles PRM and SRM will be supplementary because they are consecutive interior angles (since they share a common side and are located between the parallel lines).

The sum of supplementary angles is $180°$.

Since angle PRM and SRM are supplementary, so:

$$PRM + SRM = 180° \rightarrow 17y + 5 + 5x = 180 \rightarrow 17y + 5x = 175 \; (1)$$

Now, since LM and NO are parallel and PQ is a transversal, angles SRM and QSO are alternate interior angles.

And the measure of angle QSO is given as $90°$, so for the lines to remain parallel, angle SRM should also be $90°$:

$$5x = 90 \rightarrow x = 18 \; (2)$$

Using the value of x from (2) in (1):

$$17y + 5(18) = 175 \rightarrow 17y = 175 - 90 \rightarrow y = \frac{85}{17} \rightarrow y = 5$$

So, for lines LM and NO to be parallel with the given conditions:

$x = 18$, and $y = 5$

8. Choice C is correct.

To find the slope of a line perpendicular to a given line, you need to find the negative reciprocal of the slope of the given line.

Given the equation $y = -5x - 4$, the slope (m) is -5.

The negative reciprocal of -5 is $\frac{1}{5}$.

So, the slope of a line perpendicular to $y = -5x - 4$ is $m = \frac{1}{5}$.

9. Choice B is correct.

An has 8 reflection lines of symmetry and a rotational symmetry of 45°.

A S-shaped has no reflection lines of symmetry and a rotational symmetry of 180°.

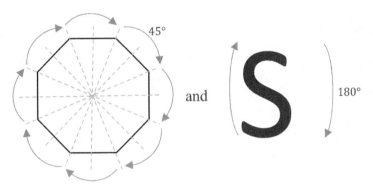

and

10. Choice C is correct.

Angle of depression, $\theta = 25°$

Distance from point P to the base of the tower, $PQ = 90$ meters

The angle of elevation from point P to the top of the tower is also 25°. Using the tangent function:

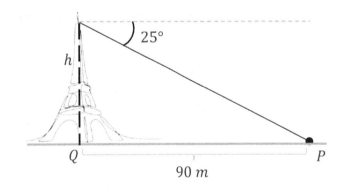

$$tan(25°) = \frac{height\ of\ the\ tower, h}{PQ} \rightarrow h = PQ \times tan(25°) \rightarrow h = 90 \times 0.466 \rightarrow h \approx 42\ m$$

So, the height of the tower is approximately 42 meters.

11. Choice B is correct.

If the two triangles share a common side and have two pairs of congruent angles, we can use the Angle-Side-Angle (ASA) congruence postulate to determine if the triangles are congruent.

In this case: Side (Given), Angle (Given), Angle (Given)

This fits the Angle-Side-Angle (ASA) postulate. Therefore, two triangles are congruent to by ASA.

12. Choice A is correct.

let's break this down step by step.

The volume (V) of a square pyramid is given by: $V = \frac{1}{3} \times base\ area \times height$

For a square pyramid, the base area A is s^2, where s is the side length. Given that the side length s of the base of the pyramid is 5, the base area A is: $A = 5^2 = 25$

Given that the pyramid is inscribed in a cone, the height of both is 7. Then:

$$V = \frac{1}{3} \times 25 \times 7 \to V = \frac{175}{3} \approx 58.33$$

The volume (V) of a cone is given by: $V = \frac{1}{3} \times base\ area \times height$

Given a square inscribed in a circle, the diagonal of the square is the diameter of the circle.

To find the area of the circle, we first need to find the diameter of the circle using the Pythagorean theorem.

Finding the diagonal (d) of the square (which is the diameter of the circle):

$$d^2 = s^2 + s^2 \to d^2 = 25 + 25 \to d = \sqrt{50} \to d = 5\sqrt{2}$$

$$r = \frac{1}{2}d \to r = \frac{1}{2} \times 5\sqrt{2} \to r = \frac{5}{2}\sqrt{2}$$

Now, the formula for the area A of a circle is:

$$A = \pi r^2 \to A = \pi \left(\frac{5}{2}\sqrt{2}\right)^2 \to A = \pi \left(\frac{25}{4} \times 2\right) \to A = \pi \left(\frac{25}{4} \times 2\right) \to A = 12.5\pi \to A \approx$$
$$39.25$$

Now, we can Find the volume of the cone, (Base area is 39.25, and height is 7):

$$V = \frac{1}{3} \times 39.25 \times 7 \to V = \frac{1}{3} \times 39.25 \times 7 \to V = 91.58$$

Therefore, the volume of the pyramid is approximately 58.33 cubic units, and the volume of the cone is approximately 91.58 cubic units.

13. Choice C is correct.

Using the Pythagorean theorem for right triangle IJK:

$$KI^2 = IJ^2 - JK^2 \rightarrow KI^2 = 20^2 - 16^2 \rightarrow KI^2 = 400 - 256 \rightarrow KI = \sqrt{144} \rightarrow KI = 12$$

Now, triangle ILK is similar to triangle IJK. Using the properties of similar triangles:

$$\frac{KI}{IJ} = \frac{LK}{JK} \rightarrow \frac{12}{20} = \frac{LK}{16} \rightarrow LK = \frac{12 \times 16}{20} \rightarrow LK = 9.6$$

Now, using the property of triangles $\triangle JLK \sim \triangle IJK$, we can find JL:

$$\frac{JL}{JK} = \frac{LK}{KI} \rightarrow \frac{JL}{16} = \frac{9.6}{12} \rightarrow JL = \frac{9.6 \times 16}{12} \rightarrow JL = 12.8$$

The area of triangle IJK is:

$$Area = \frac{1}{2} \times JK \times KI \rightarrow Area = \frac{1}{2} \times 16 \times 12 \rightarrow Area = 96 \text{ Square units}$$

Therefore, answer is 9.6, 12.8, 96.

14. The answer is 12.

We know: $V_{cone} = 450, r_{cone} = 6, V_{cone} = \frac{1}{3}\pi r^2 h$

Now, calculate the height of cone: $450 = \frac{1}{3}\pi(6^2)h \rightarrow h = \frac{450 \times 3}{36\pi} \rightarrow h = \frac{75}{2\pi} \rightarrow h \approx 11.9$

So, the altitude of the cone is approximately $12\ cm$.

15. Choice C is correct.

Surface Area $= \pi r^2 + 2\pi rh$ (for the cylinder) $+ \frac{4\pi r^2}{2}$ (for the semi-sphere without the base)

$$SA = \pi(7^2) + 2\pi(7)(5) + 2\pi(7^2) \rightarrow SA = 98\pi + 35\pi + 98\pi \rightarrow SA = 217\pi\ cm^2$$

Volume $= \pi r^2 h$ (for the cylinder) $+ \left(\frac{2}{3}\right)\pi r^3$ (for the semi-sphere)

$$V = \pi(7^2)(5) + \left(\frac{2}{3}\right)\pi(7^3) \rightarrow V = 245\pi + \frac{686}{3}\pi \rightarrow V = 473.67\pi\ cm^3$$

Therefore, the surface area is $217\pi\ cm^2$, and the volume is approximately $473.67\pi\ cm^3$.

16. Choice A is correct.

Using the angle bisector theorem: $\frac{XY}{XZ} = \frac{YW}{ZW}$

And $ZY = ZW + YW$, then we have: $ZW = 21 - YW$

From this, we can find YW and ZW.

$\frac{11}{17} = \frac{YW}{21-YW} \rightarrow 17 \times YW = 231 - 11 \times YW \rightarrow 28YW = 231 \rightarrow YW = 8.25$ units

Then, substitute the value of YW, in this equation:

$$ZW = 21 - YW \rightarrow ZW = 21 - 8.25 \rightarrow ZW = 12.75 \text{ units}$$

Therefore, answer is option A, 8.25 and 12.75.

17. Choice B is correct.

Using the property that the tangent from an external point is perpendicular to the radius at the point of tangency:

$$CD^2 = CF \times FG \rightarrow CD^2 = 5 \times 14 = 70 \rightarrow CD = \sqrt{70}$$

The length of CD is $\sqrt{70}$ or approximately 8.37 units.

18. Choice B is correct.

The formula for the measure of each interior angle of a regular polygon with n sides is:

Interior angle $= (n - 2) \times \frac{180°}{n}$

The formula for the measure of each exterior angle of a regular polygon with n sides is:

Exterior angle $= \frac{360°}{n}$

For an octagon (8 sides):

Interior angle $= (n - 2) \times \frac{180°}{n} = (8 - 2) \times \frac{180°}{8} = 6 \times 22.5 = 135°$

Exterior angle $= \frac{360°}{n} = \frac{360°}{8} = 45°$

19. Choice C is correct.

Using the general equation of a circle:

$$(x - x_1)^2 + (y - y_1)^2 = r^2 \rightarrow (x - (-4))^2 + (y - (2))^2 = 6^2 \rightarrow (x + 4)^2 + (y - 2)^2 = 36$$

So, the equation of the circle i$(x + 4)^2 + (y - 2)^2 = 36$.

20. Choice B is correct.

Since all four sides are equal, it is a rhombus. So: $3y = y + 6 \rightarrow 2y = 6 \rightarrow y = 3$

For the angles, the opposite angles of a rhombus are supplementary. So:

$$110° + x° = 180° \rightarrow x° = 70°$$

21. Choice D is correct.

In a triangle with an inscribed circle, the segments of the sides created by the tangents from the circle to the triangle are equal. Thus:

$AU = AV = 6, CV = CW = 11$, and $BU = BW = 15$

So: $AB = AU + BU = 6 + 15 = 21$

$\quad AC = AV + VC = 6 + 11 = 17$

$\quad BC = BW + WC = 15 + 11 = 26$

Perimeter of triangle $= AB + AC + BC = 21 + 17 + 26 = 64$.

22. Choice A is correct.

From the properties of triangles, the size of an angle is directly proportional to the length of the side opposite it. Therefore:

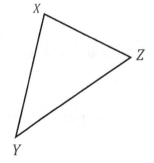

Since $(XY > XZ)$, $(\angle Z > \angle Y)$

Since $(XY < YZ)$, $(\angle Z < \angle X)$

Combining these results, the order from least to greatest measure is: $\angle Y < \angle Z < \angle X$

23. Choice C is correct.

Using the cosine function:

$$\cos H = \frac{IH}{GH} \rightarrow \cos 70° = \frac{10\sqrt{2}}{GH} \rightarrow GH = \frac{10\sqrt{2}}{\cos 70°} \rightarrow GH = \frac{10\sqrt{2}}{0.342} \rightarrow GH = 41.35$$

Using the sine function:

$$\sin H = \frac{IG}{GH} \rightarrow \sin 70° = \frac{IG}{41.35} \rightarrow IG = \sin 70° \times 41.35 \rightarrow IG = 0.939 \times 41.35 \rightarrow IG = 38.83$$

GH is approximately $41.35\ cm$.

IG is approximately $38.83\ cm$.

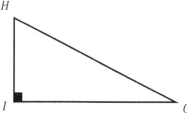

24. Choice B is correct.

From the properties of a parallelogram: $LM \parallel ON$

Using the given conditions and properties of a parallelogram:

Vertical Angles Theorem: The angles opposite each other when two lines intersect. In our case, when OP intersects LN at point Q, ($\angle LQP = \angle NQO$).

Alternate Interior Angles: Given two parallel lines and a transversal (in our case LM and ON are parallel, and OP and LN are the transversal), the alternate interior angles are congruent. Based on this:

$$(\angle LPQ = \angle QON), (\angle QLP = \angle QNO)$$

With the above angle relationships, we can conclude that triangles LQP and NQO are similar by AAA (Angle-Angle-Angle) criterion.

Since triangles LQP and NQO are similar, the ratio of their corresponding sides will be equal.

Therefore, $\frac{LP}{NO} = \frac{LQ}{QN}$. And given:

$$(LQ = LN - QN \rightarrow LQ = 7 - QN)$$

From the parallelogram's properties:

$$NO = LP + PM \rightarrow NO = 5 + 4 \rightarrow NO = 9$$

Using the side ratios from the similar triangles:

$$\frac{5}{9} = \frac{7-QN}{QN} \rightarrow 5QN = 63 - 9QN \rightarrow 14QN = 63 \rightarrow QN = 4.5$$

Then, substitute QN into this equation $LQ = 7 - QN$, to find LQ:

$$LQ = 7 - 4.5 = 2.5$$

Therefore, LQ is 2.5 units, and QN is 4.5 units.

25. Choice D is correct.

In a kite, the diagonals are perpendicular, and one of the diagonals bisects the other.

Thus, $FP = \frac{1}{2}FH$. Then, $FH = 2 \times 14 \rightarrow FH = 28$. And, $EG = EP + PG \rightarrow EG = EP +$ 24. So, first find EP.

EFP is a right triangle. So, Using the Pythagoras theorem:

$$EF^2 = FP^2 + EP^2 \rightarrow 18^2 = 14^2 + EP^2 \rightarrow EP = \sqrt{324 - 196} \rightarrow EP = \sqrt{128} \rightarrow EP \approx 11.3$$

then substitute EP into this equation:

$$EG = EP + 24 \rightarrow EG = 11.3 + 24 \rightarrow EG = 35.3$$

Now, to find FG, Using the Pythagoras theorem for triangle FPG:

$$FG^2 = PG^2 + FP^2 \rightarrow FG^2 = 24^2 + 14^2 \rightarrow FG = \sqrt{576 + 196} \rightarrow FG = \sqrt{772}$$

$$\rightarrow FG = 2\sqrt{193} \rightarrow FG \approx 27.8$$

So, $EG = 35.3$, $FH = 28$, and $FG = 2\sqrt{193}$ or $FG \approx 27.8$.

26. Choice A is correct.

Area of sector: $A = \frac{\theta}{360°} \times \pi r^2 \rightarrow 18\pi = \frac{\theta}{360°} \times \pi \times 8^2 \rightarrow \theta = \frac{18\pi \times 360°}{64\pi} \rightarrow \theta = 101.25°$

Arc Length: $L = \frac{\theta}{360} \times 2\pi r \rightarrow L = \frac{101.25°}{360°} \times 2\pi \times 8 \rightarrow L = 4.5\pi \rightarrow L \approx 14.13$ units

Therefore, the answer is option A: $101.25°$, 14.13.

27. Choice B is correct.

First, since $(GH = 24)$ and $(FG = 10)$ and given that $(\angle G = 90°)$, we can use the Pythagorean theorem to find the length of FH.

$$FH^2 = GH^2 + GF^2 \rightarrow FH^2 = 24^2 + 10^2 \rightarrow FH = \sqrt{676} \rightarrow FH = 26 \text{ units}$$

Next, we can see that triangle FIJ is similar to triangle FGH based on AA similarity since both are right triangles and share $(\angle F)$.

Let's use the ratios from these similar triangles to find IJ:

$$\frac{IJ}{GH} = \frac{FI}{FH} \rightarrow \frac{IJ}{24} = \frac{6}{26} \rightarrow 26 \times IJ = 24 \times 6 \rightarrow IJ = \frac{144}{26} \rightarrow IJ = \frac{72}{13} \rightarrow IJ \approx 5.5 \text{ units}$$

Finally, $(HJ = FH - FJ)$, use the ratios from $\triangle FIJ \cong \triangle FGH$ to find IJ:

$$\frac{FJ}{FG} = \frac{FI}{FH} \rightarrow \frac{FJ}{10} = \frac{6}{26} \rightarrow 26 \times FJ = 10 \times 6 \rightarrow FJ = \frac{60}{26} \rightarrow IJ = \frac{30}{13} \rightarrow FJ \approx 2.3 \text{ units}$$

Then, substitute FJ, into the equation $(HJ = FH - FJ)$: $HJ = 26 - 2.3 \rightarrow HJ = 23.7$

To summarize:

$$FH = 26, HJ \approx 23.7, IJ \approx 5.5$$

28. Choice C is correct.

The measure of an angle formed by two chords inside a circle is half the sum of the measures of the arcs intercepted by the angle and its vertical angle.

$$\angle STU = \frac{1}{2}\widehat{SU} \rightarrow \angle STU = \frac{1}{2} \times 160° \rightarrow \angle STU = 80°$$

29. Choice A is correct.

To reflect a point over the line $y = -x$, you switch the x and y coordinates and change the signs. So, the reflection of a point (a, b) over the line $y = -x$ is $(-b, -a)$.

Given the points:

$A(-1,3) \rightarrow A'(-3,-1)$

$B(-1,0) \rightarrow B'(0,-1)$

$C(3,0) \rightarrow C'(0,-3)$

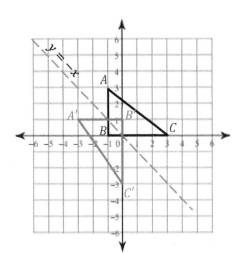

and if we draw the line $y = -x$, and draw $\triangle A'B'C'$. We can see that is true.

After reflection in the line $y = -x$:

A' is $(-3,-1)$

B' is $(0,-1)$

C' is $(0,-3)$

30. Choice B is correct.

To rotate a point (x, y) about the origin by $45°$ counterclockwise, you can use the following transformation:

$x' = x \cos 45° - y \sin 45°$

$y' = x \sin 45° + y \cos 45°$

And we know: $\cos 45° = \frac{\sqrt{2}}{2}$ and $\sin 45° = \frac{\sqrt{2}}{2}$

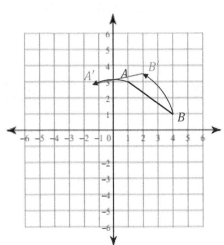

Let's find the new coordinates for each point:

For $A(1,3)$:

$x' = 1 \times \frac{\sqrt{2}}{2} - 3 \times \frac{\sqrt{2}}{2} \rightarrow x' = \frac{\sqrt{2}}{2} - \frac{3\sqrt{2}}{2} \rightarrow x' = -\sqrt{2}$

$$y' = 1 \times \frac{\sqrt{2}}{2} + 3 \times \frac{\sqrt{2}}{2} \rightarrow y' = \frac{\sqrt{2}}{2} + \frac{3\sqrt{2}}{2} \rightarrow y' = 2\sqrt{2}$$

So, A' is $(-\sqrt{2}, 2\sqrt{2})$.

For $B(4, 1)$:

$$x' = 4 \times \frac{\sqrt{2}}{2} - 1 \times \frac{\sqrt{2}}{2} \rightarrow x' = \frac{4\sqrt{2}}{2} - \frac{\sqrt{2}}{2} \rightarrow x' = \frac{3\sqrt{2}}{2}$$

$$y' = 4 \times \frac{\sqrt{2}}{2} + 1 \times \frac{\sqrt{2}}{2} \rightarrow y' = \frac{4\sqrt{2}}{2} + \frac{\sqrt{2}}{2} \rightarrow y' = \frac{5\sqrt{2}}{2}$$

So, B' is $(\frac{3\sqrt{2}}{2}, \frac{5\sqrt{2}}{2})$.

Thus, after a $45°$ rotation about the origin, the new coordinates of the points are:

$$A'(-\sqrt{2}, 2\sqrt{2}) \text{ and } B'(\frac{3\sqrt{2}}{2}, \frac{5\sqrt{2}}{2}).$$

31. Choice B is correct.

Since D is the midpoint of AC and $AD = 15$, then $CD = 15$ as well (because midpoints divide segments into two equal parts). So:

$$AC = AD + CD \rightarrow AC = 15 + 15 \rightarrow AC = 30 \text{ units}$$

Now, the Pythagorean theorem can be used in triangle AEB:

$$AC^2 = AE^2 + EC^2 \rightarrow 30^2 = 18^2 + EC^2 \rightarrow EC = \sqrt{900 - 324} \rightarrow EC = 24 \text{ units}$$

Now, to find GC:

Since $CF = \frac{1}{2}BC$, $DC = \frac{1}{2}AC$ and $DF = \frac{1}{2}AB$, so $GC = \frac{1}{2}EC$. Then:

$$GC = \frac{1}{2} \times 24 \rightarrow GC = 12$$

Therefore, $AC = 30$ and $GC = 12$.

32. Choice B is correct.

The statement "All Governors are over 35 years old" can be written in if-then form as: "If someone is a Governor, then they are over 35 years old."

Given this conditional statement, if Maria is 28 years old, she cannot be a Governor since she is not over 35 years old. Therefore, the correct answer is option B.

Description:

The conditional statement establishes an age-criteria for someone to be a Governor. Since Maria's age doesn't meet the criteria, it concludes that she is not a Governor.

33. Choice A is correct.

The given statement "If it snows, the roads become slippery" is a conditional. The logical equivalent of this conditional in its contrapositive form is "If the roads do not become slippery, then it doesn't snow." The contrapositive inverts and negates both the hypothesis and the conclusion of the original statement, making option A the correct answer.

34. Choice A is correct.

To determine the distance of chord AB from the center of the circle, we can use the properties of right triangles and the Pythagorean theorem.

Let's name the circle's center as O and the midpoint of the chord AB as M. When we draw a radius from O to the midpoint M of the chord, we form a right triangle with the radius, half of the chord, and the segment from the chord's midpoint to the center.

Therefore, half of the chord $(AM = \frac{26}{2} = 13\,)$

In the right triangle OAM:

$$OA^2 = OM^2 + AM^2 \rightarrow OM = \sqrt{484 - 169} \rightarrow OM = \sqrt{315} \rightarrow OM = 3\sqrt{35} \approx 17.75$$

Thus, chord AB is $3\sqrt{35}$ or approximately 17.75 units away from the center of the circle.

35. Choice C is correct.

This is an example of a valid argument pattern known as "Hypothetical Syllogism" or "Chain Argument." If b implies a, and c implies b, then it logically follows that c implies a. Thus, the correct conclusion is $c \rightarrow a$.

36. Choice D is correct.

For any triangle, the sum of the lengths of any two sides must be greater than the length of the third side. Using the given sides:

$$15 + 18 > z \rightarrow 33 > z$$

$$18 - 15 < z \rightarrow 3 < z$$

Thus, the range for z is $3 < z < 33$. So, the option D is correct.

37. Choice C is correct.

In triangle GHI, the side opposite the largest angle is the longest, and the side opposite the smallest angle is the shortest. Given the angles, the order of sides from shortest to longest is:

Shortest $= \overline{GH}$ (opposite $30°$)

Middle $= \overline{HI}$ (opposite $40°$)

Longest $= \overline{GI}$ (opposite $110°$)

Therefore, the correct answer is option C: $\overline{GH}, \overline{HI}, \overline{GI}$

38. Choice A is correct.

We need to determine NK and KM:

Now, if IN extends through M and onto the other side of JK, the segment beyond M, which we'll call NK, is what we need to determine for the length KM.

Given that $JN = 5$ and $JK = 7$: $NK = JK - JN = 7 - 5 = 2$

Given the triangles IJN and KNM are similar by the AA postulate, then the sides are proportional.

Using the proportionality:

$$\frac{IJ}{KM} = \frac{JN}{NK} \rightarrow \frac{9}{KM} = \frac{5}{2} \rightarrow KM = \frac{18}{5} \rightarrow KM = 3.6$$

Now, let's find the ratio of the areas of triangles IJN and KNM.

Using the property of similar triangles:

$$\frac{Area_{IJN}}{Area_{KNM}} = \left(\frac{IJ}{KM}\right)^2 = \left(\frac{9}{3.6}\right)^2 = (2.5)^2 = 6.25$$

This means the area of triangle IJN is 6.25 times larger than the area of triangle KNM.

39. Choice D is correct.

To determine the truth value of the statement, we'll break it down.

1. $\sim q$ (not q): Since q is false, $\sim q$ is true.

2. $(\sim q \wedge p)$: Combining the true value of $\sim q$ with the true value of p using "and" ($\wedge$) gives a result of true.

3. $\sim r$ (not r): Since r is true, $\sim r$ is false.

4. $(\sim q \wedge p) \vee \sim r$: Combining the true value from step 2 with the false value from step 3 using "or" ($\vee$) gives a result of true.

Therefore, the truth value of the statement $(\sim q \wedge p) \vee \sim r$ is true.

Correct Answer is A.

40. Choice B is correct.

We're supposed to find the measure of $\angle L$.

According to the vertical angle theorem angle $\angle JQK = \angle IQL$

And $GH = 180°$, so:

$$\angle IQG + \angle IQL + \angle HQL = 180° \ (1)$$

And we must find the measure of $\angle IQG$, $\angle IQL$, $\angle LQH$, to find measure of $\angle L$.

First, consider triangle IQG:

Angles in a triangle sum to $180°$. So:

$$\angle IQG + \angle I + \angle G = 180° \rightarrow \angle IQG + 55° + 95° = 180° \rightarrow \angle IQG = 30°$$

Next, consider triangle JQK:

Again, angles in a triangle sum to $180°$. So:

$$\angle JQK + \angle J + \angle K = 180° \rightarrow \angle JQK + 50° + 65° = 180° \rightarrow \angle JQK = 65°$$

So, $\angle IQL = \angle JQK = 65°$

Now, consider triangle HQL:

The angles in triangle HQL will also sum to $180°$. So:

$$\angle HQL + \angle H + \angle L = 180° \rightarrow \angle HQL + 55° + \angle L = 180° \rightarrow \angle HQL = 115° - \angle L$$

Now, Plugging this into our equation (1):

$$30° + 65° + 115° - \angle L = 180° \rightarrow -(\angle L) = 180° - 30° - 65° - 115° \rightarrow \angle L = 30°$$

So, $\angle L$ is $30°$. The answer is option B.

Effortless Math's Geometry Online Center

Effortless Math Online Geometry Center offers a complete study program, including the following:

✓ Step-by-step instructions for all Geometry topics

✓ Numerous Geometry worksheets to help you measure your math skills

✓ Video lessons for all Geometry topics

✓ Geometry practice questions

✓ And much more…

No Registration Required.

Visit **EffortlessMath.com/Geometry** to find your online Geometry resources.

Build Your Math Skills: Our Top Book Picks!

Download eBooks (in PDF format) Instantly!

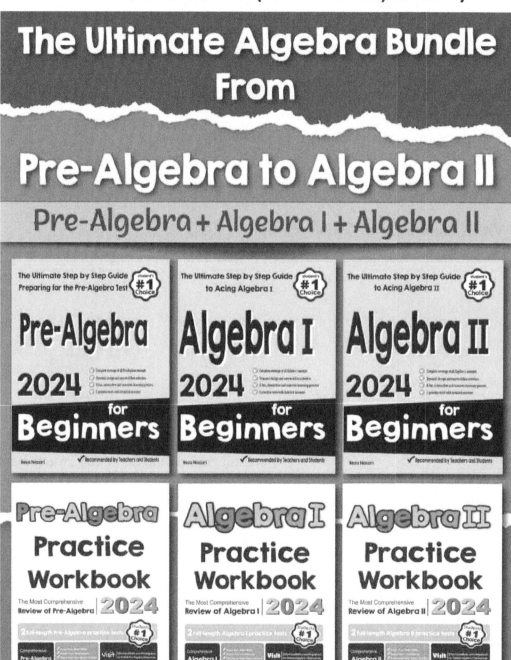

download at

Our Most Popular Books!

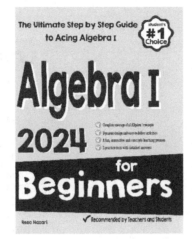

Download at **Download**

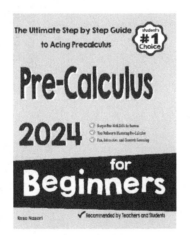

Download at   **Download**

Our Most Popular Books!

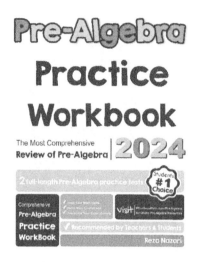

Download at

Download

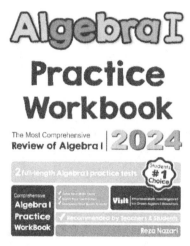

Download at

Download

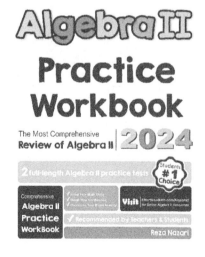

Download at

Download

Download at

Download

Receive the PDF version of this book or get another FREE book!

Thank you for using our Book!

Do you LOVE this book?

Then, you can get the PDF version of this book or another book absolutely FREE!

Please email us at:

info@EffortlessMath.com

for details.

Author's Final Note

I hope you enjoyed reading this book. You've made it through the book! Great job!

I would like to express my sincere appreciation for choosing this study guide to aid in your preparation for your Geometry course. With a plethora of options available, I am grateful that you selected this book.

It took me years to write this study guide for the Geometry because I wanted to prepare a comprehensive Geometry study guide to help students make the most effective use of their valuable time while preparing for the final exam.

Over the course of my decade-long career teaching and tutoring math, I have compiled my personal notes and experiences into the creation of this study guide. It is my fervent hope that the information and lessons contained within these pages will assist you in achieving success on your Geometry exam.

If you have any questions, please contact me at reza@effortlessmath.com and I will be glad to assist. Your feedback will help me to greatly improve the quality of my books in the future and make this book even better. Furthermore, I expect that I have made a few minor errors somewhere in this study guide. If you think this to be the case, please let me know so I can fix the issue as soon as possible.

If you enjoyed this book and found some benefit in reading this, I'd like to hear from you and hope that you could take a quick minute to post a review on the book's Amazon page.

Leave your review at: bit.ly/3tBbIsC

Or us this QR code:

I personally go over every single review, to make sure my books really are reaching out and helping students and test takers. Please help me help Geometry students, by leaving a review!

I wish you all the best in your future success!

Reza Nazari

Math teacher and author

Made in the USA
Las Vegas, NV
03 April 2024

88193812R00188